Bird of Sorrow

Bird of Sorrow

by

JOHN ROMANIELLO M.M.

*"You cannot prevent the Bird of Sorrow
from flying over your head, but you can
keep him from nesting in your hair."*
CHINESE PROVERB

P. J. KENEDY & SONS
NEW YORK

Library of Congress Catalog Card No. 56–8937
Copyright © 1956 by John Romaniello, M.M.
PRINTED IN THE UNITED STATES OF AMERICA

Foreword

THE CHINESE have a saying: "You cannot prevent the Bird of Sorrow from flying over your head, but you can keep him from nesting in your hair."

It may be asked why, at a time when so many books are being written about China, I am writing another. The answer lies in the proverb. In the history of the Chinese people, sorrow has been deep and continuous, but never has the Bird of Sorrow been able to build a permanent nest in their country. The policy of terror practiced by the present Communist regime makes it natural for many people to forget the courageous, humorous, intelligent spirit that characterizes the people of China as a whole. They may overlook the patient endurance that forever drives the Bird from its nest. All the characters and incidents in my story are taken directly from life and, although I have made changes in a number of names and places, *Bird of Sorrow* is a close record of events as they actually occurred in "Dragon Town."

It is my hope that this account of a missioner's last months in China (a missioner, I must admit, who is very like myself), and of the nobility of individuals under terrible pressures will awaken in the reader some of the sympathy and admiration I feel for the Chinese people — a people now receiving such a prolonged visit from the Bird of Sorrow.

Contents

Bird of Sorrow

1
Yellow Dust

As Father Frank Kent and I stood at the parlor window of St. Joseph's Mission watching an ominous column of smoke rising to the north, the telephone rang sharply. Starting at this interruption of my thoughts, which, centered on the Chinese civil war, were as black as the smoke, I crossed to the telephone, lifted the receiver and heard the voice of Mr. Wang, governor of Kwangsi Province.

His voice came sharp and tense to my ear. "Father Roman, will you drive me to the airfield this morning?"

At first I was too surprised to speak. Governor Wang was a friend of many years' standing, but I had not seen him for several days and had assumed he had escaped to Hongkong to join his family.

"Of course, Mr. Wang," I assured him.

"I cannot thank you enough, Father." His low voice was warm with relief. "I'll be over in about an hour." He hung up without formality.

"Frank," I cried excitedly, turning back to my assistant

who still stood at the window, "Governor Wang asked me
to drive him to the airfield! Do you realize what that
means?"

"It means, for one thing, that you'll have a dangerous
trip, John," answered Kent.

"I know, Frank, but I couldn't turn him down. Think
of all he has done for the Mission."

"You can't make the trip alone, John. I'm going along."

I touched him gratefully on the shoulder. "Fine, Frank.
And we'd better hurry. The governor said he'd be here
in an hour."

As we turned away from the window I thought of the
long comradeship we had shared. I was the pastor of
St. Joseph's Mission in Dragon Town, Kwangsi Province,
South China, and Father Kent was my assistant. We had
been together during the hardships of the Japanese war;
now we faced a new danger in each other's company. The
civil war going on around us in China was gradually add-
ing up to total victory for the Communists. The Nationalist Army was on the verge of collapse. In the past few
months the Red Army had driven southward to the border
of Kwangsi. The fall of Dragon Town was imminent.

Dragon Town — or Lung Chou as it is known in Chinese — is situated in the northern part of the vast and
mountainous province of Kwangsi. It lies on the main line
of the South China Railroad, a populous city of forty
thousand people. Dragon Town boasts a provincial university and a modern Main Street, illuminated by elec-
tricity. On the outskirts of the city there is an airfield —
Governor Wang's destination that morning.

As I went to my room to change my clothes, I heard the
boom of guns in the distance. It had become a familiar

sound in the past two weeks since Kwangsi soldiers had established defenses at the North River, eleven miles from Dragon Town. I knew that the heavy column of smoke we had seen indicated that the Kwangsi troops, before retreating, were destroying their fuel supplies at the north station of the railroad. The smoke surging in black rolls across the clear blue sky was the sign that it would be only a matter of hours before the Red Army would enter our walled city, rushing like a great flood through its wide gates. We, along with the Old China we loved, would be swept behind the bamboo curtain.

The beauty of the sunshine-filled day was an ironic contrast to the smoke billows. On the surface it was a day on which one should rejoice to be alive. However, I was anything but joyful. How I had prayed that Dragon Town where I had spent such a happy life with my good Chinese would be spared from the Red scourge. I had expected a miracle!

In my room, as I pulled on a pair of brown trousers and buttoned a blue shirt across my substantial middle, I reflected on the contrast between myself and Father Kent. I was past my prime and getting to be portly while he, in his middle thirties, was vigorous, physically fit and had a fine crop of thick brown hair. My hair was thinning out so much, I didn't need a comb any more (I flattened it out with a towel in the mornings)! Temperamentally we were equally unlike. I was impulsive, loquacious; Kent, steady and never ruffled. More and more I had come to rely on my quiet, robust young assistant. How would our stamina hold up under these impending dangers?

No matter what was to come, we had long ago decided to stay with our people. We had put ourselves in God's hands and were resigned to go into bondage with the good people of China. Anyhow, it was a relief from tension to know that the Communists were almost at our door. At least we would know what was going to happen to us next.

Pausing for a moment before I left my room, I thought of the journey ahead of us this morning. What if the Reds should intercept us on the road to the airfield — the Nationalist governor of Kwangsi and two American missioners? What would happen to us? I answered my own question. We would all hang together from the same tree. I shuddered at the thought. But I took myself firmly in hand. No matter what the risk, I admonished myself sternly, it's worth it.

Our garage was on the left side of the Mission courtyard. As I came out into the fresh day, Father Kent was checking the tires on our jeep so I got busy and filled the tank with gasoline from a fifty-gallon drum we kept on hand. Our new maroon jeep could easily make the nine-mile trip to the airfield. It was in first-class condition, a recent gift from friends in Stamford, Connecticut. On its side was painted the inscription:

DRAGON TOWN

CATHOLIC MISSION

STAMFORD, CONNECTICUT

U.S.A.

I thought affectionately of all the generous friends back home who had banded together to send us this invaluable machine; then, spurred by the need to hurry, I bent over to check the oil.

Just then Su Li, the young son of our Mission cook, Su Wen, strolled into the courtyard munching a cookie and holding a top and string in his right hand. This chubby, bright little boy was a good friend of ours and, noticing that we were preparing to use the jeep, he ran up and all in one breath cried: "Fathers, where are you going? Can I go with you?"

"We're going to the airfield, Su Li, but we can't take you with us today." I spoke firmly in a tone that Su Li recognized as "that's all; no more questions." He took the hint, but he moved over closer to me and murmured in a low, warning voice:

"Father, they say there's trouble on the road to the airfield. Three farmers were held up by bandits in daylight yesterday!" Then, stepping back, he added cheerfully: "But don't be afraid; no bandit can catch up with our jeep. It's too fast."

He capered off through the Mission gate into the glorious sunshine to seek his friends and spin tops with them in front of Wu's candy shop.

Su Li had hardly disappeared when a rickshaw drew up inside the gate. It was the governor. For a moment I scarcely recognized him, dressed as he was in Chinese costume — a long blue gown and a black felt hat. I was accustomed to seeing this small man in Western clothes.

Mr. Wang looked worried and fatigued as he climbed out of the rickshaw, and my heart went out to him. He had been a progressive governor who had made tremendous strides in the development of his province. Wang was a native of Kwangsi and had held the office of governor for twenty years. I could feel his anguish at giving up all he had worked for for so long.

The governor approached Kent and me and clasped our hands warmly.

"I cannot tell you, Father," he said, "my gratitude to you for this favor."

Then he gave us information on the military situation. "The Kwangsi soldiers are, at this moment, fighting desperately at the North River but they will not be able to hold their line. A military plane is due to leave the airfield at high noon. It will be the last plane out, and I must be on it!"

He went on to explain that by this time plain-clothed Communists had infiltrated every corner of Dragon Town. Under such circumstances his life was in danger no matter which way he turned. He was certain, however, that no one would think of him making his escape in the Mission jeep.

There was no time to waste. Gently nudging his elbow, I said: "Governor, jump in the back of the jeep. I'll drive and Father Kent can sit up in front with me."

I backed the jeep out of the garage, and headed south on Tiger Street. In front of old Madame Wu's candy shop a dozen boys were spinning their tops, Su Li among them. Madame Wu herself was drying sweet-potato chips in the sun on bamboo trays. It was a peaceful scene. Obviously, neither the boys nor the old woman was in the least concerned with the possible outcome of Communist occupation. Like millions of other Chinese they were absorbed in the pleasure of ordinary living. Political issues had no meaning for them.

We turned right on Lion Street and, noticing that the street did not have its usual lively appearance, I observed to Father Kent: "Most of the shops are boarded up. The rumor that the Reds will take the town today must be around."

He nodded, but pointed out one familiar face to me, that of our barber, Liu. He was standing in front of his shop smoking a long bamboo pipe and as he noticed the jeep go by he saluted us with a wave.

Turning on to Main Street, we noted that this thoroughfare was ominously quiet. Not even the traffic policeman, who usually stood on a traffic island under an umbrella, was visible. Most of the fashionable shops were closed. Only the carriers bearing firewood and the vegetable vendors on the sidewalks still plied their trades. Dragon Town was certainly not its bustling, commercial self today.

Leaving Main Street, we came out into the open country onto a bumpy road that wound through rice fields and rolling hills. Clouds of dust arose as we passed, coating us yellow and stinging our eyes. We passed a column of weary Kwangsi soldiers, headed south in single file. I asked the governor:

"What will happen to them now?"

He answered in a flat voice: "I suppose they will be encircled or captured by the Communist troops."

A little farther along we came to an open rice field where the only person in sight was a farmer plowing his soil. A cloud of fine dust from our jeep momentarily blotted out the peacefulness of his world. It occurred to me that for forty centuries, in peace or war, the Chinese farmer had tranquilly applied himself to tilling the earth; to him, catastrophes must have been like a puff of our yellow dust.

As we roared into the airfield, a military guard halted us at the gate. Not until Governor Wang produced his card were we allowed to proceed. Then, jolting across

the dusty field, we could hear clearly the sound of shellfire — a sound that we had not noticed during our wild
ride.

"Hurry!" the pilot shouted. "We have no time to
spare." He, too, was afraid that the Reds had already
broken through the North River defenses. Tension was
plainly written on the face of each crew member.

Governor Wang bade us a hasty farewell and thanked
us graciously for our kindness. As the motors began to
warm up he quickly entered the plane and, settling himself beside a window where he could peer out at us, waved
good-by as the plane taxied down the runway and took
off.

"Let's get out of here, Frank," I exclaimed as we dashed
for the jeep. The shellfire seemed much louder now, and
there was no cover for us in this flat, bare area. The ground
shook under our feet.

"Don't get nervous, John." Father Kent could feel my
tension. "Just step on the gas and keep going. Let's hope
the guards don't stop us again."

But by this time the guards had vanished. We drove out
of the airfield at top speed and straight down the road
back to Dragon Town. The Kwangsi troops had also disappeared.

"Where do you suppose the straggling soldiers went,
Frank? Not one of them is in sight."

"They must have fled into the hills," Kent replied ab-
stractedly.

At that moment we heard the crackle of rifle fire. It was
very close. Before we could collect our wits, bullets were
whizzing over and past our jeep. I pushed the accelerator
down to the floorboard, so that we bounced along the
rough road as if we were riding a bucking bronco.

"Keep going," Father Kent said calmly but emphatically. Instinctively I ducked my head as a fresh volley of bullets flew over the jeep.

"Frank, I think we ought to abandon the jeep," I cried. "We could take shelter in one of the embankments along the road. We might be safer there."

"Don't stop! Keep cool and hold on tight to that steering wheel. Just go as fast as you can and we'll make it."

The jeep rocked along the road in a fresh burst of speed under my nervous foot. Would we ever get back to the Mission alive?

"Don't worry, John. If we're hit our number is up, but with that dust screen you're throwing up, those sharpshooters haven't got a chance." Kent grinned at me as he spoke.

"You've got a great philosophy, Frank," I replied gloomily. "I wish I could share your optimism."

At last, however, we turned a bend in the road and the whistling bullets stopped. I had been clutching the wheel so tightly, leaning forward, intent on holding the jeep on the road, that my hands were slippery with sweat.

"Relax, John; we made it." Kent leaned back happily in his seat.

"Frank, who do you suppose shot at us?"

"It could have been the vanguard of the Red army converging on the airstrip."

"Whoever it was . . . "

I didn't finish my sentence. I was weak with relief.

As we approached Dragon Town everything appeared as normal as it had when we set out earlier, except for group after group of straggling, exhausted Kwangsi soldiers slowly retreating southward. A new column of smoke was visible over the south station. It looked as if

more fuel were being destroyed by the soldiers before they
abandoned Dragon Town altogether.

Main Street had blossomed during our absence. Now
all the shops were closed, but the street was crowded with
people and looked like a fair. Vendors were everywhere,
and bargaining appeared to be at a peak. All sorts of
merchandise were on sale. Some of the vendors were selling cotton by the yard, others offered woollen socks, bolts
of cloth, Chinese or Western clothes, cloth and leather
shoes, bamboo hats, umbrellas. One man was shouting at
the top of his lungs: "Very good fountain pens for sale.
Cheap! Fifty cents each!"

Where had they all come from? Were they enjoying their
last hours of freedom?

As we approached, our jeep was recognized and the
crowd parted to let us through. Familiar faces smiled at
us and we heard friendly voices calling, "Father." Kent
and I waved at them automatically. Our minds were still
too full of our harrowing adventure to respond whole-
heartedly.

When we passed the telegraph office, I noticed four
soldiers rush from its entrance. What was happening? I
soon found out, for we had gone less than a block farther
when we heard a deafening explosion. The soldiers had
blown up the telegraph office!

That was enough for us. The jeep jumped forward and
we swerved into Lion Street and finally reached the Mission. I wheeled into the courtyard and stopped the car
dead! Shakily I climbed out, looking ruefully at my once-
blue shirt. It was invisible under a layer of yellow dust. I
tried to rub the stinging particles out of my eyes, exclaim-
ing impatiently:

"How that grit stings!"

Father Kent, on his way to the house to wash, called back over his shoulder: "Don't gripe about that dust, John. Be grateful even for the stinging. It stung the eyes of those Communist sharpshooters today — and saved our necks."

2

Two Guests with Strange Manners

FATHER KENT picked up his pack of cards and, looking up at me, said resignedly:

"I haven't made it once tonight! I'm giving myself one more chance at this solitaire fiasco, then I'm going to bed."

He was sitting at a small table in the library of our rectory, expertly shuffling the cards with his large hands as he spoke. Standing beside him, watching his moves, I answered:

"You're distracted tonight. Your mind is on the bamboo curtain."

"No doubt about that," he replied. "Every time I play a card in this game I keep wondering what *their* first move will be."

Neither of us was able to get out of his mind the fact that the Red Army had entered Dragon Town about three o'clock this very day. From the Mission gate we had seen part of the "liberation army" triumphantly march past. The soldiers had sung loudly the Communist anthem: "No Communist Party. No China."

These tall, sturdy soldiers from North China, many of whom were immediately quartered near the Mission in the empty houses of rich merchants who had fled to the free world, contrasted sharply with the familiar, short, thin, shabbily-dressed soldiers of former days. They were clad in new dark-green uniforms, and their stature and determined bearing had made a strong impression on me as they swung by the gate, their bayonets glistening in the afternoon sun. What a pity, I had thought, that these fine-looking men had to be part of a Chinese *Red* Army.

Nevertheless, in spite of the arrival of the soldiers, this evening I almost felt relieved that the confusion and uncertainty seemed to be over. During the past six months thousands of merchants and landlords who could see no hope of survival in their native land under the new regime had passed through Dragon Town by train, in trucks or in donkey carts, as they fled to safety in Hongkong. For weeks Dragon Town had been a no-man's-land. Now the immediate anxiety was past and I was not yet quite ready to consider the future.

"At least," I remarked to Kent, "it will be quiet tonight for a change. We can get a good night's sleep."

Father Kent, who unlike me slept peacefully under any circumstances, went on with his game without answering. I couldn't help but admire his outward calm and his ability to force himself to concentrate on the cards. Now, however, he was blocked in his moves. I pointed to the ace of hearts — it was under his nose, but he hadn't noticed it.

He gave me a sheepish look. "I must be sleepy. I didn't see that move."

Deciding that I had interfered with his game enough, I was about to say good night when I heard the front door of the rectory creak open.

I glanced at my wrist watch. "What! Visitors at this hour?" I said irritably. "It's after ten o'clock."

Light footsteps in the corridor identified our caller. "That's Su Li," I exclaimed in surprise. "I wonder what he wants so late."

Su Li's shaven head appeared round the door. His two black slits of eyes for once were wide in his moon face as he cried out: "God bless you," in the usual salutation used among the Christians.

"Two soldiers are in the courtyard, Father." He held up two fingers to impress his news upon us. "They want to see you, Father. They said I should tell you they're sorry to come so late. They said they'll come back to-morrow if you can't see them. Shall I tell them you'll see them, Father?"

Without thinking, trying to put off the evil day, I replied: "Su Li, tell them to come back tomorrow."

"Tomorrow, Father?" There was a note of doubt in Su Li's voice. I could see that he did not favor my idea of postponement.

I turned to Father Kent. "Do you think it's important that I receive them tonight?" I asked him.

"I think it is important, John," he answered me gently. "They are our first Communist visitors."

"Su Li," I said, after a moment's deliberation, "tell the soldiers to come in. Father Kent has spoken wisdom."

Su Li ran out quickly to tell the unexpected visitors

that I would see them. Provoked and slightly nervous, I said to Father Kent:

"Remember the rumor we heard that the Reds have the unpleasant habit of arresting people in the middle of the night and carting them off to a jail where they are never heard from again? This may be *my* night, Frank." I was half-teasing, half-serious.

"Then I'll go along to jail with you." He grinned. "We can't let the Communists break up this team after all the years we've worked together."

"Oh, no, Frank," I countered. "You'll have to stay behind and take over here."

He eyed me knowingly. Kent's love of the simple missioner's life and his distaste for administrative duties were subjects about which I often teased him.

"I've got a feeling," he said, flicking the cards, "that you just want someone who will bring you your soup in jail. I hear the Reds don't like to waste food on prisoners."

"Well, Frank," I answered with a chuckle, "if I don't come back you can have my alarm clock."

"Thanks, John, but I'd rather have you get me up. You're better than an alarm clock. I can't turn you off."

I walked over to the clothes rack in the corner and picked off my hat and coat. "I'll probably need these in jail," I remarked casually. "The night is turning cold and Chinese jails are said to be airy!"

Father Kent whistled softly — his signal that he knew he was being teased. I replaced my hat and coat on the rack, went to the front door, and turned on the courtyard lights. Su Li was standing outside with the two soldiers. He looked very tiny alongside them, for both were tall; one, thin, the other heavy and broad.

"Come in, come in," I called warmly. I heard my voice ring out into the night and was annoyed to hear it quaver.

The stalwart soldiers approached and blocked the doorway. For a moment they gazed into the parlor, then they turned their stares on me. A quiver of apprehension went through me as they eyed me up and down. Were they anticipating trouble? Were they planning how to control me if I got out of hand? In their towering presence I felt very small and helpless.

From their position at the door they were able to see the windows on both the right and left sides of our parlor. Why were they so interested in the windows? Were they contemplating methods of escape? I was puzzled by their strange behavior. I began to get restless standing there at the door waiting for them to come inside.

"Enter," I repeated cordially. "You are welcome."

At this second invitation they came in without uttering a word. The only sound they made was the noise of their heavy footsteps on the wooden floor of the room. To reassure myself I attempted to make conversation with them, but they did not answer me, and refused to sit in the chairs I offered them. Instead, they examined the room wordlessly, with particular attention to the pictures hanging on the walls.

As I prepared to serve them tea, they took up a stand in front of a colored picture of the guardian angel. It was an attractive picture. The angel was clad in a white gown and had golden wings. He was watching over a little boy, dressed in a blue suit, gleefully chasing a butterfly, unaware that he was crossing a plank over a deep mountain ravine. As they studied the painting I said to myself: I hope my guardian angel is at my side tonight!

From the painting of the angel they turned their attention to the crucifix hanging on the wall of the parlor. I held my breath and kept my eyes fixed on them. As they examined it they shifted their eyes back and forth between the crucifix and me. What was in their minds? I was afraid they intended to remove the crucifix from the wall and break it. Such an idea made me shudder. What would I have done?

A portrait of the Holy Father caught their eyes next. The thin soldier pointed to me, but the broad soldier shook his head. They moved on to our small bookcase, where they stopped and began to finger the books, flipping over some of the pages. What could they be looking for? Of course I could ask them. Did they speak English? I wondered.

At last, having inspected the room to their satisfaction, they sat down. I poured the tea, and, in accordance with Chinese hospitality, with both hands presented a cup of tea to the tall, heavy soldier. He made a motion with the back of his hands, indicating that he declined to have a cup of tea with me. The other soldier also refused the tea.

This was unheard of — to refuse to accept this traditional Chinese gesture of courtesy. Were they Chinese? Of course. Yet their manners were not Oriental. Their rudeness astonished and provoked me.

I was wearing a short, loose-fitting jacket with wide sleeves — native Chinese dress — and from one of the pockets I pulled out a pack of cigarettes. I offered one to the first soldier; he again declined with the same motion of his hands. I stepped up to the thin soldier and said to him:

"Have a smoke?"

In a cold, hard voice, he answered: "No!"

He had spoken! I had heard a sound even though it cut like a knife. Our eyes met and immediately I felt uncomfortable. His eyes were small black beads filled with evil. His general appearance was rough, his countenance pockmarked. I saw with alarm that he carried a revolver.

Earlier in the evening I had only been joking about being taken away to jail; after seeing this hard-looking soldier I was not so sure it was a joke. I felt I was no longer in my own home; the parlor had become a den. They were fierce lions and I was their prey. When they were ready they would devour me. They were in no hurry. I had no avenue of escape.

I wanted a cigarette myself but I refrained from lighting one for fear of offending them. I no longer felt like a host receiving guests. I was only being tolerated by these two dominating, strong-willed soldiers of the Red Army. Nevertheless, I would not accept defeat. I attempted to get control of the situation by asking the tall, heavy soldier:

"What is your honorable name?'

He did not answer my question. Instead, as I was standing up, he commanded in a low, melodious voice:

"Father, please sit down."

I was astounded at his sweet voice. Perhaps I shouldn't have been surprised, since this second soldier was an attractive, pleasant-looking man. His voice was persuasive and I obeyed his command unthinkingly. I was invited to sit down in my own parlor!

"Father," he said, when I was seated, "we have come to listen to your radio. We have been informed that you have one here at the Mission."

I was too dumfounded to answer. I pointed to the radio on the opposite side of the room.

"We are interested in hearing the newscast from Peiping at ten-thirty," Officer Soft, as I mentally named him from his voice, said politely.

"Certainly," I responded, completely confused as to why they had come to me to hear the newscast. I arose from my chair and inadvertently glanced at Officer Hard, as I thought of the other soldier, who was sitting at right angles to me. I saw with horror that he was deliberately pointing his revolver at me. I was so struck with terror that I sank back into the chair, unable to move.

"Please, Father," came the gentle voice of Officer Soft once more. "We would like to hear the news on the radio."

His voice sounded far away; I was dazed with fright.

"Of course," I agreed, half-heartedly. My eyes were glued on Officer Hard. His revolver was now directed at my stomach. These soldiers won't even take me prisoner, I thought. While the radio is on — very loud — Officer Hard will shoot me.

"The radio, Father, if you please!" Officer Soft ordered again. The contrast between his polite voice and his companion's actions distracted my reason. Certainly I must be having a nightmare.

I forced myself out of my chair and, going over to the radio, tuned it in to the Peiping station. I was not out of range of the gun, but since it was now aimed at my back, I felt safer, unreasonable though it might be. I leaned over the radio, and twirled the dial, trying to collect myself. I felt freer now that I was on my feet and was easily able to shift out of the gun's range. Even though Officer Hard moved his gun in my direction, although without looking at me, I had a certain satisfaction in the thought that if he *did* fire I was in a position to dodge. My corpulence might slow me down but I had a chance.

While he listened to the broadcast, Officer Hard relaxed his aim and twisted his revolver in his fingers. My feeling of safety increased. I was even able to listen to the broadcast. The two officers appeared pleased when the newscaster praised the People's Liberation Army, and rose to their feet when he prophesied that under its great leader, Mao Tse-Tung, the Chinese People's Republic would in ten years become one of the most powerful nations in the world. While they listened to his words, they appeared to have forgotten I was in the room.

When the newscast was over I felt sure that my uninvited Communist guests would depart. However, they sat down again.

"Are you a Catholic priest?" asked Officer Soft in his friendliest tone.

"I am," I answered quietly.

"We admire Catholic priests for their great devotion to the people."

This remark, so obviously false, aroused me. I had recovered from my fear sufficiently to wish to assert myself. Fighting an impulse to snatch the gun away from Officer Hard, I deliberately lit a cigarette and asked boldly: "Why does your companion keep his gun leveled at me?"

Officer Soft smiled. "I have been wondering why you are so nervous, Father. You need not be alarmed. Do not mind my friend. He is the hero of our regiment and is suffering combat fatigue. He is really as harmless as a child."

"He would be absolutely harmless with a wooden gun," I retorted.

"You are belligerent, Father!"

As he spoke I glanced at Officer Hard once again. His hand was on the trigger as he contemptuously glared at me. He squeezed the trigger, and I instinctively threw my arms up before my eyes. I heard the click of the hammer and shrieked. The shrill sound of my voice vibrated in the room. Instantly I heard the mirthless snicker from Officer Hard. The gun had not gone off. Had it been empty?

A chill ran down my spine at the thought of what might have happened had the gun been loaded. I was perspiring so freely that I had to take out my handkerchief and wipe my brow, neck and hands. I could feel my fury rise at having to perform this humiliating act in front of the two grinning officers. I had demonstrated that I wasn't so brave as I had hoped to convince them I was.

For the second time Officer Hard spoke in his sharp voice: "Tell the foreigner about the two Catholic priests I arrested as spies in Hunnan Province, north of here."

"Oh, yes, Father. That was unfortunate. Of course we know that *most* Catholic priests are good men." Officer Soft's voice was apologetic.

"I don't believe it!" I retorted, gesticulating angrily. I stood up in the middle of my parlor and glared scornfully at my two nocturnal guests. My agitation made no impression on them. They had said what they had come to say: *"Some* Catholic priests are spies." *That* was their message! Without another word they got up abruptly and walked out of the rectory.

I was alone. I heard my own voice announcing to the empty room: "I don't believe it. Catholic priests aren't spies." How flat it sounded — how silly I was, talking to myself too late. Why wasn't I made of steel like the two soldiers? I hung my head like a whipped dog and turned off the light in the courtyard, locking the door before I returned to Father Kent.

When I walked dejectedly into the library, I found him fast asleep at the table, his head resting on his large hands, the deck of cards neatly stacked in front of him. Hearing my footsteps, he awoke and, dazed, stared at me with his mouth open.

"What happened, John? You look white and sick!"

"I died a thousand times in the last hour," I told him.

I lighted a cigarette, and sat down and told him the whole experience. "And this," I wound up, "is probably only the beginning."

Despondent, I retired to my room, reflecting that after twenty-five years in Dragon Town I had made a fool of myself and failed to live up to my mission. For the first time I began to understand the old Chinese proverb — to learn what it meant to have the Bird of Sorrow nestle in my hair.

3

Dragon Town Meets New Rochelle

M Y EXPERIENCE with the soldiers had left me drained but wakeful. My mind was much too active to think of going to bed immediately. Perhaps if I found something to read it would relax my mind and I would be able to calm down enough to get some sleep before dawn.

Stooping over to look through my bookcase, my eyes fell on a volume I had not noticed for many months — an old picture album. I picked it up to put it to one side, out of my way, but as I did so it opened to a snapshot of a smiling boy wearing a blue-serge suit with short trousers buckled at the knees. In his hand he proudly held a diploma. It was myself in 1914 on the day of my graduation from St. Joseph's parochial school in New Rochelle, New York.

As I looked at my long-ago self, so pleased and compla-cent, the idea of finding a book vanished. I remembered, suddenly, that the very occasion when this picture had been taken formed an important link in the chain of events that had brought me to China. I carried the album over to the bed, and settled myself to recall the first intimations I had had of my future life in Dragon Town.

A month before my graduation from grammar school, my teacher Sister Grace had asked each one of our class to write a composition on what we wanted to be now that we were almost finished at St. Joseph's. I had no hesitation. I wrote a paper on my desire to become a missioner and go to China.

A week later, during study period, tall and dignified Sister Grace came down the aisle to my desk and placed my composition before me. Pointing to the paper, her bright blue eyes fixed on me, she asked: "Did you write this?"

Studying the many corrections she had made of my misspelled words and poor sentence construction, I was almost afraid to raise my head, but I looked up timidly and said, "Yes."

"Do you really mean what you wrote?" Her tone was so stern that I was convinced I was in for a scolding.

Again I looked up into her strong Irish face, wondering why she seemed so displeased with me. "Yes," I repeated honestly, keeping my eyes fixed on her.

"You will never become a missioner if you don't first become a better boy, John," said Sister reprovingly.

My head dropped as I thought of the hours spent doing penance for my continual mischief. Sister Grace's usual punishment was to make the offender kneel before a statue of the Blessed Mother that stood on a pedestal in a corner of the classroom. I knelt there almost every afternoon for the last half-hour of the school day while Sister Grace told stories to the class.

Looking up at the tall Sister, I promised earnestly: "Sister, I will honestly try. Really I will."

"Then come and see me after class." She turned and walked back to the front of the classroom.

After class, as I stood beside Sister Grace's desk, I thought of the day she had related the story of St. Francis Xavier, the greatest missionary of them all. It was this story that had prompted my desire to go to China. Now, when Sister asked me if I were serious about it, I assured her that indeed I was — that there was nothing I wanted more. She spoke to me with great seriousness about the vocation of the priesthood, and I listened attentively, delighted that she believed in me.

"Run home now, and tell your father all about this," she finished. Without waiting for more, I set off for home, bursting with joy.

My parents had emigrated from Italy in 1900 and had settled in New Rochelle where my short, stocky father, Charles, worked as a ditchdigger for the water company. He and my pretty, slender mother had brought my brother, who was now married, with them from their hamlet at the foot of the Apennines. I had been born in New York. We had very quickly become a happy American family. I considered now how my father was going to feel about my leaving the United States for another country. As soon as we were seated around the supper table that night I told him that, after graduation, I wanted to study to be a missioner and go to China.

He stared at me, his fork in the air. "You mean, son, you want to be a priest?"

"Yes, yes," I cried, "but I want to be a priest in China. A missioner goes to China."

"China! China!" he repeated after me. He was silent, trying to recall just where China was. "You mean the native country of the Chinese laundryman on Sixth Street?"

"Yes, that's it; that's where I want to go."

"But that is very far away!" he said in dismay.

My spirits dropped. "I know," I answered in a low voice.

"What is the matter with you, John?" His voice was bewildered. "Is not the United States big enough for you?"

Just then a neighbor came in to borrow my mother's baking board, and quickly my father changed the subject. He did not want the neighbors to think that his son would talk such nonsense. For the time being the question of China was dropped.

At school the next morning Sister Grace asked: "What did your father say about your idea?"

"Sister, he just said: 'Isn't this country big enough for you?' "

Sister tossed back her veil and laughed. To keep me from becoming discouraged she gave me the life of St. Francis Xavier to read.

A few weeks later, in the middle of June, graduation day arrived. The pastor, Father Massi, presented our diplomas and when it was my turn to go forward, he playfully held mine back and turning to the audience, announced: "I don't believe I will give this boy his diploma. He's crazy. He wants to go to China."

There was a burst of laughter from the audience and I saw my mother's cheeks flush with embarrassment.

Nevertheless, Father Massi's joking only convinced me more strongly that this was what I wanted to do with my life.

Several days after graduation Sister Grace called me to the convent. She had important news for me. "John," she said happily, "I have found out where you can apply for entrance to the preparatory seminary. Sister Alma tells me that a Father James A. Walsh has started a society in Ossining, New York, for boys who have a vocation to go to China. I want you to write a letter to Father Walsh for application to the seminary. Then bring your father to see me so that we can get his permission."

I sat down right then and there and drafted a letter for Sister Grace's inspection. She went over it carefully, correcting my haphazard spelling; then I copied it over in ink. I could hardly believe that I was taking my first step toward China.

The minute my father came home that evening, I seized his arm and asked: "Will you come to the convent with me tonight?"

He shrugged a little. "What for?" he asked, surprised.

"Sister Grace wants to see you."

My father gave me a long look. I think he guessed why she wanted to talk with him. After supper the two of us walked the ten blocks to the convent. I rang the bell and Sister Grace opened the door for us. She led us to the small chapel where the three of us knelt to pray. My father looked shy. He had never been inside a convent before in all his life. He made the sign of the Cross and whispered a Hail Mary.

When we finished our prayers, Sister Grace took us

into the parlor. On the table lay a letter that Sister Grace had written stating that my father granted me permission to prepare for the priesthood and to go as a missioner to China. She read it aloud slowly, then, turning to my father, she asked him if he were willing to sign it.

My father picked up the pen hesitantly. "I guess that's what he wants. I don't want to stop him, Sister. It is a good thing to be a priest." He shook his head slowly. "But a missioner — that I'm not sure about."

Sister Grace smiled at him and said gently: "It is even better — to go to China."

"John," he said with sudden decision, "I sign. You be a good boy." Laboriously he wrote his name across the bottom of the letter.

Sister Grace put her arm around my shoulders. "Take the letter and mail it at the corner," she admonished me, "and on your way out, stop in the chapel and say a Hail Mary."

Feeling important, I mailed the letter. I could not have been happier.

A week later the answer came addressed to me. For the first time in my life mail meant something to me. The application was the first letter I had ever written and now I had one in return. Filled with delight, I ran straight over to Sister Grace and let her open it. Father Walsh's answer was encouraging. He asked me to fill in the application form he had enclosed and to visit him on a Sunday as soon as possible.

On the appointed day, the last Sunday in June, I presented myself to Father Walsh who received me kindly and laid his hand on my head. I felt sure that this was a sign of his approval. My life as a missioner was about to begin.

Smiling a little at the remembrances the snapshot had called up, I got up and replaced the album in the bookcase. What a lot of years had gone by since my first visit to Father Walsh. I had spent twelve of the happiest of them preparing for the priesthood until, on June 17, 1927, I was ordained at Maryknoll, Ossining, New York. In September of that year I at last sailed for China. The following year I spent in Pengnam, studying the Chinese language, and when that was over I was assigned, with a fellow priest, to open a mission in Dragon Town.

We had been told beforehand of the beauties of Kwangsi Province whose capital was Kweilin, ancient Imperial city of South China. I could hardly wait to get started — to see with my own eyes its famous palaces and clifflike mountains — the originals of the scenery in some of the loveliest Chinese scrolls.

Actually we got to see very little of the scenery. We traveled via the back of a peanut truck and my clearest memory of the Kwangsi mountains is of viewing them while sacks of peanuts rumbled down on us, or as we were suddenly tossed onto the knobby sacks ourselves.

When we finally arrived in Dragon Town, a kind old woman showed us the way to the house rented for us. She obviously felt sorry for us. We were foreigners who had been taken advantage of. The house, she told us, was haunted! As soon as I saw its high, gloomy walls and tumbledown appearance I knew how it got its reputation.

No one was there as we approached our new rectory, although our Chinese houseman was supposed to be on hand to greet us. (Later we discovered it had taken several full days for him to make his farewells with all filial affection to his aged grandmother.) In the meantime we looked with dismay at our house — the walls covered with moss, the woodwork in decay, the doors split and sagging, the roof eaves cracked, with wildflowers and weeds growing out of them.

Luckily we were able to get a good meal in a nearby restaurant that night. This gave us strength to round up some sawhorses and boards so we would not have to sleep on the damp floor. The next day — it was the Feast of the Holy Rosary — we said our first Mass in Dragon Town, and then set to work with a will on our tumbledown rectory.

First we carried the moldy furniture outside and swept, scraped and scrubbed the house from roof to floor. Then we came out to the yard with our brushes and washed the furniture with soap and water. The old caretaker next door watched with interest and amazement. When we were through, he approached me and said earnestly: "In all my seventy years I never saw so much energy expended on mere dust."

Our once-haunted house became a bright and friendly place during the years that followed. We got to know every family in Dragon Town; we became good friends with the Baptist minister and his wife, our only fellow Americans. Soon the familiar life I had known back in New Rochelle and Ossining became as faraway and unreal as life in China had seemed to my father the first day I told him I wanted to become a missioner.

Whereas in my boyhood I had been used to swim and

fish in Long Island Sound, now I learned to love the beautiful Fu (Bitter) River, which flowed just behind our Mission. It got its name because of its strong currents and swift rapids. I never tired of looking at it as it flowed by — clear as crystal, an enormous long mirror reflecting the steep little hills and twisted trees along its banks, the fleecy clouds overhead. According to Chinese poets, water and mountains form the basis of all beautiful scenery. Here we had both these important elements in all their glory. No wonder the beauty of Dragon Town was a favorite subject for the ancient writers of South China!

As the years passed, Dragon Town and our Mission suffered heavily from the devastation of the Japanese war. The larger buildings of the town — including our rectory — were bombed. For many months our parish house and church were located on a houseboat in the rushing Fu River.

But all these circlings of the Bird of Sorrow had passed away. Dragon Town had been rebuilt. Our Mission was stronger and firmer than ever—not only in its structure but in the hearts of the people. Now, once more, all was threatened. In my mind's eye that night the great dark bird flew down closer around the city that was a second home to me.

Overcome by my powerlessness to ward off the danger that was swooping so near to all of us, my mind grew dull and drowsy. At last I fell asleep lying across the bed.

4

The "American Chicken" Raises a Siege

NEXT MORNING I sat down at my desk to look for a letter I had recently received from a reporter friend back home. His letter should have been on the top of a batch, but I must confess that I don't keep an orderly desk. As a result, I had to rummage through the entire drawer before I found it.

The reporter had written prophetically: "You have chosen to stay in China but you are doomed; the Reds hate Americans, and you will be labeled a spy." After last night's ignominious ordeal I perceived the truth of his prediction. It occurred to me that it was no longer prudent to keep old letters, much as I liked to. I knew there was nothing really incriminating in them, yet I was afraid to have them fall into the hands of the Red officials. They might misinterpret the contents to condemn me as a spy. I decided to destroy them all.

I began with the letter from my reporter friend, and as I was tearing it into a hundred pieces, I glanced up and saw

Su Li at my open door. As usual he was holding a cookie
in his hand and his jovial face was like a ray of sunshine.
My ill-humor left me, and I banteringly exclaimed:

"Su Li! You're eating again! You'll get so big that you
won't be able to walk, and then you'll have to waddle like
a duck. The children of Tiger Street will call you 'Fatty.' "

"They call me that now, Father," Su Li answered buoy-
antly. "Besides," he continued boastfully, as he patted his
little stomach, "my roundness is proof of your goodness
and kindness."

We laughed together, and I retorted, "You have something there, Bright One!" I often called Su Li that when
he gave forth a smart answer.

"Father, the two soldiers who were here last night are
in the courtyard again."

"Oh, no!" I groaned. "I would rather see the devil."

Su Li was so astonished by my sudden burst of ill-
temper that his cookie fell to the floor and he did not even
bend down to pick it up. I felt my cheeks flush with anger
and I resentfully growled at innocent Su Li:

"Tell the soldiers I am not at home! Tell them anything. I don't want to see them."

Su Li stared at me in great consternation. This was the
first time he had ever seen me in a turbulent state of mind.

"Father," he said timidly, "they say they've come on
official business."

I got up from my desk and stood beside the window in
my room. As I gazed on the clear waters of the Fu River
sparkling in the morning sun, I felt my surge of indignation recede. I spoke more gently to Su Li.

"In that case, Su Li, wait here a minute. I must see
Father Kent."

I found him in the library.

"The two soldiers are back, Frank, and I hate to see them again."

"I don't blame you," Father Kent said sympathetically, "but the shock of their actions last night is over now, and you will be on your guard for the second round."

He was right, of course, but I tried to find a way out. I had been so shaken by the Red visitors' dreadful intimidation that I had no heart for a second encounter.

"I don't trust myself, Frank."

"That's your best guarantee. The main thing is, keep a cool head, John!"

"All right. Here I go — into the 'Red ring,' Frank. If I'm knocked out, remember, you'll have to take over the parish."

"Keep your dukes up, John, and you'll be back," Father Kent admonished me, with a wide grin.

In better spirits I left the library and returned to Su Li who was comfortably seated in my rocking chair. He was swaying back and forth and munching his cookie, the picture of perfect contentment.

He shouted enthusiastically to me: "I'm riding your wooden horse to hunt the tiger."

I nodded and said: "Su Li, go tell the soldiers that I will see them in the parlor."

He instantly jumped out of the chair, and ran to the courtyard and delivered my message. As I entered the parlor, I observed the two soldiers outside the door, awaiting my arrival.

When Officer Soft saw me, he said politely: "Father, have you had breakfast?"

"Yes," I replied in a civil tone. Remembering last night's visit, I had not expected such a proper manner of approach.

I was glad I was wearing my cassock. A priestly robe seemed more formal than a Chinese gown when I had to face two soldiers on official business for the Chinese People's Government.

"Come in, come in," I said cordially, as if I were receiving devoted friends.

"Sorry to trouble you, Father," Officer Soft said graciously. He had the air of one who was grateful to have the opportunity to visit me.

"It's no bother at all," I responded, carrying out the ceremony of hospitality.

The two officers entered the parlor and removed their caps. That was another act of respect I had not anticipated. They stood in the middle of the parlor until I asked them to sit down.

"You have a heart, Father," Officer Soft replied. His comment meant, "Thank you, Father." I could hardly believe my ears.

While they sat decorously in their chairs, I stepped to the small serving table in the corner of the room and poured out two cups of tea. I ceremoniously presented Officer Soft with a cup, and, as he received it, he stood up and said:

"I am not worthy to have the Father wait on me." His remark was in accordance with the rules of Chinese etiquette, yet I was surprised to hear him say it to me, especially in his silver-toned voice. I served Officer Hard and even he grunted and bowed as Chinese sometimes do when they express their gratitude without words. Was I in a dream world?

I offered them cigarettes, which they accepted with a great demonstration of appreciation. Officer Soft even stood up to light my cigarette.

We were seated at right angles to each other, as we had been the previous night, but how different it was! Officer Hard had no gun, and his beady, piercing eyes were not concentrated on me. Nonetheless, while externally I appeared collected and serene, I had a nervous sensation in my stomach.

Officer Soft introduced himself in Chinese fashion:

"My humble name is Captain Fu Tan, and my comrade's honorable name is Captain Sun Ming."

I responded: "My worthless name is Lo Man."

What a magnificent display of Oriental propriety!

Captain Fu then explained that they were connected with the Military Security Police.

"We are sorry to have come to annoy you, Father," Captain Fu declared, "but it is our official duty to interrogate you as a matter of formality."

"It is only reasonable," I replied in the understanding tone of a superior man. (A superior man, according to Chinese culture, is one who possesses a magnanimous soul, even in the presence of his enemies.)

"Are you an American, Father?" Captain Fu asked.

"I am," I answered gently. As I said it, I noticed that Officer Hard, whom I now knew by the name of Captain Sun, stirred in his chair at the mention of the word "American."

"Have you an American passport?" the captain inquired.

"Yes, I have an American passport."

At this Captain Sun leaped out of his chair, as if he had been stung by a bee, and went over to the window. He had a painful expression on his rough face which intensely exaggerated his ugly appearance.

I glanced at Captain Fu apprehensively.

"Father," he replied, "the honorable name of your country has an exasperating effect on Captain Sun. The sound *Mei-Kuo* — beautiful country — America, arouses a flame of hatred in the depths of his heart. He blames America for all the evils in the world." Without pausing he added: "May I see your passport, Father?"

I was glad he did not say "American." If he had, I am sure that Captain Sun would have strangled me.

I went to my room to get it. When I returned, Captain Sun evidently had recovered from his indignation for he was seated in his chair again.

Captain Fu received my passport without a comment. He examined it thoroughly page by page. In a notebook he copied information from the passport. When he had completed his examination, he passed it to Captain Sun. Would he tear it to pieces? He copied the number of my passport on a card.

As he returned it to me, he roared: "Communists in America are hunted; Americans in China are free! How do you explain such American justice?"

What a change from our earlier rites of politeness! A conciliatory answer seemed impossible, yet I hated to be the one to arouse his fury at my country. How I wished that I could speak out man to man.

Suddenly in the courtyard outside the rectory door there arose an angry guttural sound; it was the gobble-gobble of a turkey cock! The two officers stared at each other, puzzled, because they had never heard such a sound before. The noise was one I'd come to know well in the last few days — the voice of the Mission gobbler, a parting gift to our Mission from Governor Wang.

The two officers did not even have time to rise when,

without a by your leave, there appeared at the door our
proud, haughty gobbler with his colorful, fanlike plume.
He garrulously strutted into the parlor.

After one quick glance around, he charged straight for
sullen Captain Sun and took a nip at his shin. The astonished captain swung his long leg viciously at the gobbler. He retreated momentarily, then charged obstreper-
ously again.

The "hard" captain was furious. If he had carried his
gun, he would have shot the handsome, feathered bird on
the spot. He would probably also have taken a shot at me
as the responsible proprietor.

As for myself, I wished for an earthquake so that the
earth might open up and swallow me. I was mortified,
and at the same time so frightened that instead of doing
something about it I merely sat in the bamboo chair petri-
fied. My mask of Oriental composure had vanished.

Suddenly Su Li rushed in to the rescue carrying a small
basket of fragrant warm rice. Loftily the proud bird allowed himself to be lured from the "field of battle."

"Kill that American chicken," the enraged captain
shouted over and over. In my perplexed state of mind I
forgot that "American chicken" was the local Chinese
name for turkey. I was sure that he meant me!

Su Li slowly led the gobbler to the pen behind the rectory. In the parlor a threatening silence was broken by
Captain Fu, the soft-spoken soldier, who quietly asked me,
as though nothing extraordinary had happened:

"Father, are not American chickens, or fire chickens as
we call them, rare here? Where did you get this one?"

How was I to answer his question? Should I mention
the former governor's name, or not? I decided to tell the
truth.

"It was a present from Governor Wang of Kwangsi Province," I replied.

"So you are a friend of the governor, Father?" Captain Fu asserted in a manner that indicated he was pleased to hear it. "How close were you to the governor, Father?"

"Ordinary friends," I answered serenely.

"You should have said, Father," Captain Fu corrected me sharply, "that you were close friends; you drove him to the airfield the day we liberated Dragon Town."

This was the first time I had noticed a note of irritation in his conversation. I sat tranquilly in my chair, and looked straight at Captain Fu without anxiety or fear. It seemed to me he was disappointed in my reaction. I held on to my mask of Chinese etiquette. I played the role of the superior man perfectly. Inwardly, I regretted that the turkey cock had rudely interrupted our bout of nerves.

"Father," Captain Fu said, "we are sorry to have taken up your valuable time."

"Not at all," I responded with good grace.

The two Communist officials rose from their chairs, stepped outside the front door, turned around, bowed, and departed like two stars acting in a drama.

I wished to apologize, but it would have made matters worse. What could I say that would soothe this affront to their dignity?

Suddenly outside in the courtyard I heard a crackling sound. Just beyond the window I saw Su Li striding ahead of the two captains and holding a string of sputtering firecrackers. He was performing the ancient Chinese custom for honored guests, as a gesture of atonement for the turkey's misbehavior — an insult for which I was certainly held responsible!

I was proud of courageous Su Li and of his quick-witted

father Su Wen, who had come to my rescue with this ceremony of reparation.

Father Kent had heard the commotion and he stood in
the corridor observing it all. After the captains had departed, he joined me at the front door of the rectory to
watch the little boy shoot off the "firecrackers of atonement."

"That stupid turkey!" I exploded.

"Don't say that!" Father Kent exclaimed, laughing.
"Why, the American chicken fought on your side like a
gallant knight."

"How about the consequences?" I asked. "I might have
been shot!"

Father Kent went on chuckling. "I can't help it, John."
He shook his head. "I could hear the three of you being
so hypocritically polite — and it was like a breath of fresh
air to see the honest, barbaric manners of our pugnacious
American chicken!"

He smiled at his mental picture, and in relief I laughed,
too. Together we cheered the American chicken!

5
Young Ma Tells His Story

AT THE SOUND of a polite voice I looked up from my book to see Ma Chung, the young secretary of the Mission, standing in the doorway of my room.

"Father," he said politely, "may I come in to you for a minute?" This was his customary greeting no matter how often he came to my room — and sometimes he came twice a day.

"Come right in, Ma," I invited. "Where have you been? I haven't seen you for the past three days."

I offered the tall young man a cigarette and took one for myself. Ma, in his graceful manner, struck a match and first lit mine, then his own. After this little ceremony he drew up a chair and sat down. Ma had come originally from North China and had been employed at the Mission for three years. I was very fond of him and wondered what had kept him away. Now he answered my question.

"Captain Fu has given me work to do and I have been unable to come, Father."

"Oh!" I exclaimed. "You have met Captain Fu!"

"Yes, Father, I have. Do you not know that Captain Fu is a northerner?"

"I assumed that he was from his speech and manner, and also his height." I nodded.

"He is from the northern section of the city of Mukden in Manchuria," Ma said gravely.

"That's fine," I declared. "Perhaps he knows your family."

"It is what I fear, Father." Ma's face was impassive as he went on. "You may have forgotten that my father was a magistrate in Mukden who caused the arrest of about a hundred underground Communists. When Mukden was finally taken by the Red Army, my father was jailed and then executed. After I fled to Peiping, I went to the courts and had my name legally changed to Ma, the family name of my mother. I was afraid to use my father's name Lun. A friend, the same who had advised me to change my name, sent me to Kwangsi to study at the university here in Dragon Town."

I was ashamed that I had not recalled this at once. What could I say to reassure him? Before I could speak, Ma added slowly:

"I have been thinking, Father, that it would be well if I were to escape to the hills."

"But Ma, isn't it too late now?" I queried, alarmed at his daring. "It's too bad you didn't disappear before the Communists came." I went on, not looking at him directly: "How about Li Li Pan?"

Li Li Pan was the daughter of a Chinese Standard Oil merchant in Dragon Town, a beautiful girl who had come often to the Mission with Ma Chung. I knew that he was very much interested in her.

Ma got up and went over to the window, his face averted. "Li Li Pan is already in the uniform of the Red Army," he answered bitterly.

"What!" I shouted. Could it be possible that such a charming girl as Li Li Pan was a Red? He nodded, barely controlling himself. It was true.

"So that's it!" I said heavily. "Well, I don't blame you for wanting to go to the hills." Without further discussion I went to the safe, removed some money and handed it to him.

"My blessing, Ma Chung, and God go with you."

He took the money, thanking me gratefully, and disappeared down the corridor.

Again the Bird of Sorrow descended on my head. I liked Young Ma and had hoped that one day he would marry his beautiful Li Li Pan. Her defection and Ma's proposed escape were my first serious blows under the New Order. My heart was sore. Furthermore, thinking of Young Ma's precarious position, I began to imagine what would happen if he did not get away.

Does Li Li Pan know Ma's background? Perhaps she does — they were so friendly. Will she give him away out of spite and resentment at his failure to follow her into the Party? Suppose he gets caught trying to escape to the hills? He will be brought back to Dragon Town in disgrace. The Reds might hang him by his thumbs — perhaps even from a tree in the Mission compound, right before my eyes.

Unable to bear such morbid thoughts, I went in search

of Father Kent to distract myself and to seek consolation. Father Kent was in his room, drawing Chinese characters.

"I'm practicing to improve my brush strokes," he greeted me happily, as if we were both living in Paradise.

Ignoring his remark, I exclaimed wildly: "Ma Chung is escaping to the hills!"

Kent put down his brush and looked up at me in astonishment. "How strange! Doesn't he know he hasn't got a chance? Didn't you tell him so?"

"He told me that registration doesn't begin until tomorrow for Tiger Street, so he thinks he still has a chance to get away."

"Did you encourage him to go?" Kent's voice had an edge on it.

"Not exactly, but I did wish him good luck and I gave him some money."

"John!" Kent threw up his hands. "Don't you realize that if he is missing, the Reds will blame you?"

"To tell you the truth, Frank, I only thought of what a wonderful young man he is. I felt so sorry for him when he told me that Li Li Pan had joined the Reds that I didn't think of the consequences. I just told him to go with my blessing."

"And all I can say is that Young Ma will hang with your blessing," Father Kent snapped, and walked out of the room.

It was the first time I had ever seen Father Kent angry in the ten years we had been together. In a belated effort to repair my mistake I went out into the courtyard to find Ma. His room was dark. I called Su Li to ask him where his father was, but Su Wen had gone to a people's meeting called by the Reds. Sad and discouraged, I turned away and went to my room.

Tonight I was not even tempted to read. I went straight to bed but, tired as I was, I found it impossible to sleep. I twisted with shame at my thoughtlessness. Why hadn't I consulted Father Kent sooner? As I tossed and turned I asked myself the one question that could give me hope: Had something prevented Young Ma from leaving?

6

Our Cards Are Nailed Up

Early next morning my prayers and questions were answered. Young Ma came in to return the money I had given him. His face was haggard and he told me that Captain Fu had kept him occupied with registration papers until daylight so that he had had no chance to carry out his plan. In true Oriental fashion his features were composed so that it was impossible for me to guess what he was feeling.

"What are you going to do now?" I asked.

"I shall meet the challenge, Father," he answered firmly. "Never shall I be a Communist." Abruptly he changed the subject. "Now I must go, Father, for Captain Fu has ordered me to register the families who live on Tiger Street. Later, I will return to take care of the Mission registration." With that he was off.

At ten o'clock Young Ma returned. All of us, Father Kent, Su Wen, his wife Mei, little Su Li and I were assembled in the parlor. Young Ma had brought our registration cards with him and they were obviously not intended for a file cabinet. Each card was as large as a poster and made of heavy yellow paper. Those for Father Kent and me were on top, labeled: "Registration of Foreigners."

Ma Chung addressed me: "Father, you are first. I will fill out your card for you."

I stood beside him as he wrote in the information:

Name:	Lo Man — John Roman
Country:	United States of America
Place of Birth:	New York City, New York
Present Address:	Catholic Mission, Dragon Town
Occupation:	Roman Catholic priest
Age:	54
Length of Time in Dragon Town:	25 years
Owner of Guns:	No
Camera:	Yes
Radio:	Yes
Broadcasting Set:	No

Young Ma indicated that these questions were all I would have to answer. "May I fill your card out now, Father Kent?" he requested courteously.

I must mention that Young Ma spoke with us in English. He had specialized in English literature at the university, and in the three years he had spent with us at St. Joseph's Mission he had improved his English conversation to the point where he could converse with ease in the language.

When Father Kent was finished, the Su family were registered together on one card:

Names:	Su Wen
	Su Mei (wife)
	Su Li (son)

Province:	Kwangsi
Place of Birth:	Su Wen — Pine Village
	Su Mei — High Field
	Su Li — Dragon Town
Occupation:	Su Wen — cook
	Su Mei — laundress
	Su Li — student
Employed by Whom:	Father Roman, American Catholic Mission
Education:	Su Wen — none
	Su Mei — none
	Su Li — G.S.
Age:	Su Wen — 35
	Su Mei — 30
	Su Li — 10

The Sus had originally had four children. During the Sino-Japanese War the family had fled to the mountains outside Dragon Town. There two girls and a boy had died from malignant malaria. Only our Su Li was left.

When he had filled out his own card as well, Ma Chung said: "Now it is necessary to list the domestic animals."

Su Li was delighted and curious. "The American chicken, Ma? And the cat and the pig and the hens?"

Ma Chung laughed and answered in Chinese: "Yes, Su Li, those are the domestic animals."

"Frank," I said in a low voice, "the American chicken may turn out to be a source of trouble for us. I hate to see Governor Wang's name put on that card."

Father Kent nodded. "Especially since it states at the bottom of the registration cards that they must be hung on the door outside the house."

Impatiently I waited for Young Ma to fill out our gobbler's form. I took it from him quickly as he finished it.

Name: *Hus-Chi* — Fire Chicken (the common Chinese name for turkey)
Origin: America
How Obtained: Gift from Governor Wang
Weight: 20 pounds

Su Li was dancing with excitement. "Where will we hang the American chicken's card?" he cried.

"It must be hung on the door of his pen," Ma Chung answered him.

"That's what I don't like," I muttered worriedly. I had noticed that the Red soldiers had formed the habit of drifting into the Mission courtyard as they passed by. The gobbler was an unfailing source of attraction to them. He amused them by spreading his plume and strutting around his pen and there were usually several of them hanging over it watching the big bird. Now, when they noticed the registration card — with Governor Wang's name on it — they would connect me politically with the Nationalists. And Governor Wang was officially listed as a political criminal!

"Father Kent," I said irritably, "that turkey will be my downfall. I think I'll have Su Wen kill it and put it in the pot."

Young Ma spoke up, a note of caution in his voice. "The American chicken has been registered, Father. If you wish now to kill it, you must first have the permission of the Security Police. I understand your feelings, for I, too, am in an unpleasant situation. When my registration card is hung on my door, 'Mukden, Manchuria,' will arouse curiosity among the soldiers. Many of them come from Mukden or nearby. There will be many conjectures and suspicions about why I am in Dragon Town. Especially, they will wonder why I work for you."

A silence fell on all of us and wordlessly I passed cigarettes to Young Ma, Father Kent and Su Wen. My worry evidently showed clearly, for Ma said gently:

"Do not let the Bird of Sorrow rest on your head, Father."

How I admired him! It was he about whom I was most concerned, for he was in danger, and on top of it, Li Li Pan had been swallowed up in the Red movement. Yet his loyalty and courage were unwavering. Here he was, consoling me, a priest!

"It is time that I leave," said Ma Chung. "Captain Fu has ordered me to complete the registration of the north end of Tiger Street before nightfall."

He crushed out his cigarette, and picked up his own registration card and borrowed a hammer and nail from Su Wen. From the front door of the rectory I watched him hang the card on his door. Father Kent nailed up ours; Su Wen hung his next; and then little Su Li, who had charge of feeding the domestic animals, hung their signs in the proper places.

As I watched Su Li a shiver went through me again just to think of the black marks put against us all by the presence of our bold and handsome American chicken.

7

Hell Is a Sense of Loss

YOUNG MA ordinarily did the banking for St. Joseph's Mission, but at the moment Captain Fu had him firmly anchored in his employ registering the families on Tiger Street. It looked as if I were going to have to take over this task myself, and, in any case, I had that day received a notice from the new People's Bank requesting that I appear in person to fill out forms and sign a new signature card.

I seized on the opportunity to leave the Mission for both Father Kent and I had been shut within the compound for two weeks and I, for one, longed to see the world outside — to catch sight of a friendly face that might give me new courage to face the bleakness of life within our walls. I suggested to Father Kent that he come along, too, but, although the idea appealed to him, he felt it might not be prudent for both of us to be away at the same time. Yesterday, he said, he had counted a hundred wounded soldiers from the nearby convalescent hospital, spending their afternoon in the Mission compound admiring the American chicken.

"How shall I dress?" I asked Father Kent. "In my clerical clothes or in Chinese fashion?'

He voted for my black suit and hat. I objected. Then
Kent repeated what Su Wen had heard Captain Fu say:
"The foreign priests wear Chinese apparel to simulate
that they are Chinese and so, unnoticed, they perform
their secret duties as American agents." Su Wen was obviously vexed with the way the wind was blowing and,
like all Orientals, while he would not directly communicate such an unfavorable remark to me, in an effort to
keep me out of trouble he had told Father Kent who had
taken care that I heard it.

Grumbling, I followed Father Kent's advice. I would
have preferred to wear my long, flowing, black Chinese
gown in which I felt more at ease. I had come to enjoy the
freedom of this loose garment and now found my own
tight-fitting clerical suit irksome. As I stepped out of the
rectory I was properly and uncomfortably clothed in my
American clothes, including leather shoes — a change from
the soft cloth Chinese shoes I was fond of wearing.

As I crossed the courtyard Su Li looked up from his
play. "Father," he shouted, "you're all dressed up in West-
ern-style clothes!" It was the first time in three years that
he had seen me dressed in this manner, and that was when
I returned from the United States, where I had been on
home leave.

How happy I had been that day to see the friendly faces
of the Sus after my year's absence. To watch Su Li dancing
around me with a string of firecrackers sputtering in his
hands, joyfully welcoming me back among them. What
made me remember that occasion this morning? Was it
the clerical suit? Or was I beginning to feel the constrain-

ing atmosphere of the bamboo curtain blight the China I loved so much.

Now Su Wen approached me and I could see strain on his countenance. He seemed already to have lost the easygoing manner of his ancient race. Was the Old China I knew passing away?

"Father," he said, "when you go out you must first go to the police substation at the north end of the street for a pass. The People's Government now names our district the north zone and the new People's Bank is in the central zone. The new law demands a pass when a man goes from one zone to another."

Father Kent had mentioned restrictions, but I was glad to get exact details from Su Wen. From the tone of his voice and his facial expression I could see that he was concerned about my welfare. Knowing that I was inclined to be careless and easily made mistakes, he tried to impress upon me the tremendous importance of proper procedure — the dominating disciplinary objective of the new Red order in China.

I thanked Su Wen for his help. As I started out the Mission gate I met a group of soldiers entering the courtyard. They glared at me out of the corners of their eyes — or so it seemed to me. *"Mei-Kuo-Jen —* American Man," they shouted in hostile tones as they brushed by me on their way to the back yard to stare at the American chicken.

Their taunt increased my consciousness that I was a foreigner, an outsider. In the past I had taken pride in the fact that I was considered a Chinese; not because I looked like one, but because I had become part of China. I remembered that Governor Wang, in a speech at a dinner party, had once called me "the first citizen of Dragon Town." Now my vanity was beginning to wane; in the last three days the Red soldiers had made me clearly understand that I was a *foreigner* and, therefore, by Oriental standards, only to be tolerated.

I paused outside the gate and looked up and down the street. Where were the people whom I knew? I asked myself. As far as I was able to see there were only soldiers on the street. Some were armed with rifles and bayonets, standing on guard in groups of three in front of the larger buildings. Other soldiers were coming and going with packs on their backs in groups of six or eight. A feeling of depression came over me. Wasn't this Tiger Street? I had lived on this street for twenty-five years, why should I feel so strange to be out on it now? I knew each house and could call by name the people who lived in it. I knew the chickens and pigs that roamed about. Wang's three pigs were grayish and had black spots painted on their backs; Li's hens next door to the Mission each had a red string tied to its leg; the Han family across the way (they were Mohammedans) kept two black goats with small bells around their necks. The telegraph poles, the willow trees — I recognized them, yes, but they also seemed strange.

I was lonely, and I was tempted to turn back. I became conscious of my size — a rice diet and Chinese cooking are not the best means for keeping slim. My one black suit, bought years ago, was a little tight around the middle and I tried to make myself inconspicuous by bending forward. The unaccustomed pressure of my hat was heavy on my head. As I slowly walked toward the police substation I took it off five or six times to air my head, I was perspiring so much. Also, holding it in my hands and doodling with it relieved my nervous tension. It seemed to me I was lost on the most familiar street I'd ever known.

I ambled along slowly behind a group of soldiers. They were talking to one another, and twice they laughed heartily. I sensed that they were laughing at me, but their northern dialect was unfamiliar. Like most of the soldiers in Dragon Town, I presumed that they, too, had come from Manchuria.

In front of a low adobe house I saw an old man whom I knew basking in the sun. He was Old Man Ku, the wood dealer. He was seated on a stool smoking a bamboo pipe. Beside Old Man Ku a husky soldier was swinging an ax vigorously as he chopped up an old stump of camphor tree into firewood. I had been told that the Red soldiers helped people in their leisure time; here, I actually saw one in action with my own eyes.

Several other soldiers were standing in the door, watching their comrade work. At the side of the house there was a brown mule and another soldier was cleaning him with a brush. I longed to talk to Old Man Ku, for he was the first familiar person I had seen outside the Mission since the Red "turnover."

He didn't look my way though I suspected that he saw me. He pretended to be busy chatting with the soldier who was performing the act of charity.

I had known that old man for fifteen years — and this day was one when I yearned to have him recognize me because I was so forlorn — but he ignored me and I was deeply hurt. I learned later, however, that Old Man Ku purposely refrained from paying any attention to me because those very soldiers had urged him to denounce the

American priests at St. Joseph's Mission. Old Man Ku had said he knew of the foreigners, but that he had nothing to do with them. I also found out later that Su Wen had communicated this information to Father Kent.

When I passed by, the soldiers shouted: *"Mei-Kuo-Jen pu ho* — American, no good."

Old Man Ku sat motionless on his stool, and I was sure his stare meant that he considered me a rare oddity, a strange creature in black, since black clothes are not common in China. In my suspicion I misjudged Old Man Ku — and I never saw him again.

I was utterly dejected when I finally reached the Confucian temple at the north end of Tiger Street where the police substation was located. The old temple was dilapidated from the weather, and from lack of repair, but it still reflected the grandeur of Chinese architecture with its steep yellow tile roof and graceful upcurved eaves.

Three soldiers armed with rifles were standing guard at the entrance. Behind them was a large, faded, blue Chinese screen that hid the interior from view. Over the entrance, identifying the police substation, was a newly painted sign that read:

KUNG-ON-FEN-CHU

As I approached the guards challenged me. Two ordinary Chinese had passed by unchallenged, so I presumed that I was stopped because I was a foreigner dressed in black clothes. To the guards I was an absolute stranger.

"Old Man," one guard asked dryly, "what is your business?" (Old Man is a term of politeness in China.)

"I wish to obtain a pass to go to the central zone."

"Old Man, go behind that screen," he said as he pointed toward the large entrance.

As I passed through, I overheard the guard say, "Who is the outlandish foreigner?" I didn't hear the answer; it was just as well, for I felt I was no longer a familiar figure on Tiger Street — but, rather, a stranger from Mars.

Behind the Chinese screen I entered a spacious hall of the temple. The red pillars that held up the rafters were faded and the whole interior looked drab from neglect. From pillar to pillar counters had been built. New wood had been used and the counters stood out in sharp contrast to everything else in the temple that reminded me of the past. Where formerly had stood the Confucian tablet of worship with the joss-stick urns there was now a large portrait of New China's great leader, Mao Tse-Tung.

Behind the counter, seated at desks, were a dozen soldier-clerks. I stepped up to the counter nearest the entrance and a clerk got up from his seat and came to me.

"Old Man," he said, "what is your business?"

He was scrutinizing me with piercing eyes. I imagined he was passing judgment on my black suit. I informed him I wanted to go to the New People's Bank in the central zone.

"Your name?"

"Lo Man."

"Nationality?"

"American."

"Address?"

"Catholic Mission, Tiger Street."

"Purpose?"

"Business at the People's Bank."

He wrote the information down on a yellow identification card and gave it to me, with the admonition that it was good only until six o'clock that day.

It was three o'clock according to my wrist watch and I checked it with the wall clock hanging from the faded red pillar near me. As I turned to depart, he said:

"Hold the pass up in your hand so the guards can see it as you leave the entrance."

I held the yellow identification card as he had instructed and passed the guards unquestioned. Like a child who needed discipline, I was beginning to learn how to follow directions. In the old days when I went to the police station, usually on an errand of mercy, the chief of police received me as an important person and I was always served a cup of tea. But here the clerks were no more than polite — and all business. My prestige had dropped to zero.

The truth was that my pride was hurt. I should be more humble, I told myself. I tried to console myself with the saying: a humble man has no difficulties. But it takes more than a pious thought to overcome the first shock of being despised and ignored.

Humiliated, I decided to take the back alleys to the central zone. From the police substation I turned left on Water Alley, named after a stream close by. Soon I ran into a hundred more youthful soldiers who had been drilling in an empty lot off the alley. All of them stared at me; I was the man in black, an object of curiosity. I longed for the power to make myself invisible from their hostile, searching eyes.

As I drew near, a guard said: "Old Man, your pass."

I pulled it out of my pocket and presented it to him. As he examined it, other soldiers gathered around me. My black hat was their chief object of interest.

"Who is he?" several of the soldiers asked at once.

"A Russian," one volunteered.

The guard said caustically, "American." With that, they all stepped back and glared at me as one to be shunned.

"American, enemy of China," they shouted in unison.

I wanted to shout back: "It isn't true," but it would have been futile. They deliberately turned away from me. With a leer on his face, the guard thrust the pass back into my hands and I slowly moved on.

Water Alley ran past some vegetable gardens. This area was suitable for cultivation because of the small stream nearby that supplied water.

Here in a spacious abandoned plot I saw about twenty boys and girls of college age. They were dressed in the dark-green uniforms of the Red Army. Some of the boys had removed their jackets but the girls had not. Several boys were raking, while others were spading the ground. A few girls were carrying the small stones in baskets to the edge of the stream; more were planting tender lettuce plants where the ground had already been prepared; still others were carrying water in buckets from the stream.

I recognized the group immediately. I had been their English professor and their youthful faces were very familiar to me. They were senior students who would graduate in June from the provincial university, the sons and daughters of rich merchants and landlords — members of the scholar class.

As I observed their activities, I could see that they were not accustomed to manual work. Under the New Order, students were being initiated in the use of their hands in gainful employment. I found out later that this group was participating in a special drive to increase food production in Dragon Town.

As I drew near, several students working close to the alley recognized me. I judged from the expression on their faces that they wanted to call to me, but they hesitated. Instead, they stared, and then turned away.

But one of them, Feng Mei, a vivacious girl, came forward, and hailed me in English: "Good afternoon, Father. Have you come to hold class in this vegetable patch?" Her voice sounded so friendly that I felt I was once again in Old China among my friends.

"I should like to," I replied, momentarily forgetting my plight.

"Classes will be resumed next week, Father. Are you coming to the university?" Feng Mei inquired.

"I don't know," I answered.

Then Feng Mei came closer to me and whispered: "There are rumors at the university that you are leaving Dragon Town because of ill-health. We will miss you, Father," she added affectionately.

"We will miss you," I repeated to myself. These were the first kindly words I had heard that day, and they were soothing to my wounded heart.

But the friendly feeling dissolved like a bubble. Before I could reply, I was rudely awakened. A surly boy student whom I did not know came forward and said scornfully:

"Who is this foreigner?"

"He is Father Roman, from the Catholic Mission; the professor of English literature at the university."

"So *this* is the American professor?" he shouted insolently. "Look at his fine capitalistic clothes!" he snapped, pointing a finger of scorn at me. "Behold the enormous size of the foreigner. He has a round belly like a rich merchant!" he yelled. I immediately drew in my waistline. Luckily my sense of humor came to my rescue. I retorted, laughing: "Scholar, you're perfectly correct. I am a *Pan-Tse*, 'Fatty,' and under the New Order I'll have the opportunity to reduce very easily."

Feng Mei picked up her baskets and walked away toward the edge of the stream. She would have no part in the abuse heaped on me. Here at the vegetable garden I was tasting of both the sweet and the bitter!

Beyond the sullen student I observed another beautiful girl amid a circle of the boys. It was Li Li Pan, and she was so attractive that her baggy uniform could not hide her charm. Her sparkling, brown, slanted eyes and her soft cheeks ever ready to dimple with a smile mirrored the joy of life. Of the twenty-odd students in the vegetable garden I knew her best because of her association with Young Ma. But she pretended she did not know me.

She remarked tantalizingly: "Who is the new foreigner?"

I suppose she referred to my black suit. The boys gathered around her howled, for they knew that she was purposely being sarcastic. Under the New Order she had changed completely.

I was mortified, stung again, but I had nothing to say. How to explain her attitude? Why had she changed so suddenly? Life is sweet; life is beautiful. No one wants to throw it away. I didn't — and I was old. Li Li Pan was young and pretty, and she wanted to live. She *had* to be a Red or die. Her family was rich and it was rumored that it was a special privilege for the rich to live under the People's Government in China.

I left the group with the Bird of Sorrow perched on my shoulder. I had intended to go straight out to Main Street, but I changed my mind. I couldn't bear to meet any more people whom I knew, so I decided to take the less-frequented Carpenter Alley to reach the central zone.

This little street was officially named Carpenter Alley because the shops on both sides of the alley were exclusively engaged in coffinmaking. The ordinary people had nicknamed it Coffin Alley. It was so narrow that I was almost able to touch the gray walls of the dingy shops with outstretched arms. The sun shone only at high noon on the uneven flat stones. As I strolled on, I had a full view of the interiors; the shops were wide open, and in every one a finished coffin was on display.

I watched the carpenters at their work. Some were sawing the slender trunks of pine trees into proper lengths while others were joining the finished pieces. The buzz of the saw and the sound of the tap-tap-tap of the wooden mallets blended together. Others were painting the completed caskets a dark-brown color. I smelled the aroma of camphor wood and fresh paint. In one shop I noticed an old man with white hair and a silver beard ordering a coffin. I heard them talking — bargaining is the zest of life in the Orient. Again I felt as if I were in Old China. There was no change in Coffin Alley — the carpenters were too busy to stop and watch me pass by. People who passed glanced up so as not to bump into me, but aside from that they had no interest in me. It was a comfortable feeling to be unnoticed for a change.

The men were absorbed in their own problems. I heard one say that his brother had been arrested the previous night. He was in jail now. He had taken his brother food this morning, but had not been permitted to see him. He said in a low tone (I was close to him so I heard his remark):

"This new government is mysterious; it arrests people without apparent reason."

I thought to myself: the Chinese are very reasonable people — will they endure this mysterious government?

I looked up to find myself in front of a shop that bore the name "The Everlasting Box Company." A sturdy brown coffin, with the character "Happiness" carved in gold paint at the head, had been set near the door. The somber thought occurred to me that perhaps on my return from the People's Bank I should invest some money in a coffin, have it delivered to St. Joseph's Mission, and store it in the guestroom for the day of my departure from this beautiful world. That day seemed near at hand this afternoon.

It is not at all strange for a Chinese to order a coffin in advance. It is common practice for opulent Chinese sons, out of filial piety, to prepare caskets ahead of time for an aged father or mother. But I suppose I would have been the first foreigner to have followed this Oriental custom.

In this morose state of mind I turned right on short Rice Lane. The rice shops were boarded up; I learned later that they had been closed by the People's Government for inventory. Rice Lane was deserted and I passed unmolested. In my fear I hurried to reach Main Street.

Main Street runs north and south through the center of Dragon Town. It is wide, and paved; it also has sidewalks. The important retail shops are clustered in the center. On that day, at four o'clock, it was crowded. On the telegraph poles I observed pale blue signs with the new name,

Mao-Kai, Mao Street — named after the new leader of New Red China. Most of the people entering or leaving the shops were soldiers, and for the most part they were visiting the novelty shops and small restaurants. Groups gathered on the sidewalk in front of stands where vendors were selling fountain pens; large groups also gathered at the watch shops.

The military police were directing traffic. I saw at least a dozen Russian-made trucks go by, in convoy. To my surprise, I also saw our maroon Mission jeep on the street. The "Stamford, Connecticut," painted on the side door was very conspicuous. The top of the jeep was down, and four stern, officious-looking soldiers were riding in it. I was astonished and resentful that our jeep had been commandeered by Red officers.

The military police were also directing pedestrian traffic. Formerly, in China, one walked where he pleased. But now the Reds were disciplining the people. Those going south had to walk on the right side of the street; those going north had to keep on the left. The M.P.'s signaled to anyone who was proceeding on the wrong side.

One old woman cursed them roundly as I passed by.

"This is all nonsense," she yelled angrily. "How can I deliver my eggs?"

Heckling the M.P. who was obstructing her path, she continued, "You stupid sweet potato! I have customers on both sides of this street!"

Calmly the M.P. instructed the old woman:

"Serve your customers on the right-hand side of the street first; then cross over and come down the left side."

One thing struck me as very strange: bicycles were very popular on Main Street, but almost the only persons I saw cycling were soldiers — everybody else walked. This fact was brought to my attention more forcibly when I saw a portly merchant, dressed in a striped gray suit and felt hat, ride by on a bicycle. He was rudely stopped by one of the military police. I saw the bulky M.P. point to the stout man's clothes; he jerked the man's hat off and made a gesture as if to throw it away; he pulled violently at the striped trousers, and at the lapel of the coat, as if he wished to tear them. I began worrying about myself as I was dressed in my black clerical suit and was afraid he would come over and make an example of me.

Just then three prying M.P.'s squeezed past me. The first one whispered caustically: "Foreign devil!" and the second murmured derisively: "American devil!" "Behold his outlandish clothes!" uttered the third resentfully. These disparaging remarks, although I had heard them before, wounded my pride. I could not reconcile myself to the unfavorable state into which I had fallen in the New China.

At last I saw before me the bank, a three-story, modern, red-brick building situated on the right side of the street. Two alert M.P.'s stood guard in front of the bank. As I approached the entrance, they challenged me, and one guard leveled his rifle, with a fixed bayonet, at my protruding stomach. No matter which way I turned I seemed to be confronted by ubiquitous M.P.'s who were suspicious of me because I was an American. To them, I probably appeared as an evil person whose motives they could not understand. I wondered why they permitted me to remain alive.

With a trembling hand I showed my pass to the guards who stepped aside reluctantly and allowed me to enter the People's Bank. I almost wished I were entering a jail, for the ever-present military police made it distasteful to be out on the street. They were spoiling the enjoyment I normally experienced in mingling with the people on Main Street. I delighted in the salutations of the market place, but the M.P.'s with their scathing remarks made me feel as if I should withdraw from the world.

The bank was bustling with activity. Merchants and soldiers mingled together at the various counters. With a heavy heart I joined the crowd and stood in line to negotiate my business. I recognized many of those standing in line with me: genial Lu of the Silk Tailor Shop, smiling Wang of the Electric Supply Company, shrewd Ho, the gold dealer — I could name each one of them.

I nodded to the men; they acknowledged it but that was all. Formerly, we would have had a smoke together, gossiped about the news and inquired about the health of our mutual friends. Now we all waited in silence. No one ordered us to keep silent, but already my Chinese friends realized that friendship with me was dangerous and frowned upon by the new regime. They were concerned about their positions as merchants in the new society. Would they be permitted to live or would they die because they possessed wealth?

I noted that even smiling, talkative Wang, who had prided himself on his association with an American electrical firm, now stood rigid, the soft lines of his countenance taut. And farther down the line I saw a slight man dressed in a long blue gown, his usually pleasant face stern and sad. It was Pan Lun, father of Li Li Pan. I longed to speak to him and offer him my sympathy, but I knew that for his sake I must say nothing.

Most of the clerks at the windows had been with the old bank. Thin, wiry Lin with the horn-rimmed glasses, who always handled the Mission business, bowed slightly when he caught my eye. He was a warm friend. Formerly he had been a cashier but now he was in charge of the signature cards. As we bent together over the form he said softly:

"Father, word has come from my native village that my father and mother have been executed for treason."

I couldn't believe it! Lin's father had been a county magistrate under Governor Wang. This news was such a shock that I became confused and signed my name on the wrong form. Poor Lin! He had to discard the first forms and make out a new set for me. I pressed his hand sympathetically. He betrayed no outward emotion, but no doubt his heart was aching as he performed his duties as bank clerk under the People's Government. How he must have hated working for the New Order that had been responsible for the murder of his parents.

Lin began to take care of the next person in line and a stout clerk in army uniform issued a new checkbook to me. I wrote out a check and presented it to still another clerk, one with whom I was well acquainted. It was Kan, Dragon Town's famous basketball star. Kan took my check and gave me a brass tag — Number 25.

"Father," he directed me, "seat yourself on the bench until your number is read out."

I sat down on the bench opposite the cash department with relief. I began to picture the bank as an inferno where my friends who were in agony dared not express their sorrow and where I could not show them my sympathy. We were all bound by steel chains of fear and this was our excruciating punishment. I glanced resentfully at a huge portrait of Leader Mao on the back wall of the bank. I wanted to shout in protest, but fear checked me and I hated myself for being a coward.

As I waited I picked up a copy of the *Red Star Daily* that lay beside me. I wanted to tear up the paper publicly but I didn't have the courage to do so. "Life is sweet, avoid unnecessary trouble," buzzed through my bewildered head. So I buried myself in the newspaper and feigned interest until my number was called.

The friendly clerk, Kan, helped me tie the bills in the blue handkerchiefs I had brought along. Since Chinese money is bulky and I did not want to have to return for several weeks, my money made a sizable pile. Kan made two neat bundles for me. I thanked him warmly for his kindness and walked to the door where the guards took my blue packages, opened them and counted the stacks of bills. They then checked the money with a statement that Kan had sent to them by a bank messenger so that I could be properly cleared — the customary procedure before a customer was allowed to leave the bank.

When the inspection was over, one of the guards returned the packages, snarling: "America, no good."

I snapped back sarcastically: "Yes, I know!" I had already heard that a hundred times today.

When I reached the street the crowd had thinned out and the sun was casting long shadows. In an hour, I reflected, it will be dark. It was evening rice time and as I passed the open doors of shops I could see the shopkeepers and their clerks seated at round tables, eating. Their usual joviality had vanished — worry was registered on their golden-skinned faces.

The fragrance of cooked rice flowed out of the shops and I felt a pang of hunger. It increased when I ran into

witty Old Man Fan bent over his iron pan, roasting chestnuts.

"Hot chestnuts, Father!" he called as he saw me coming
down the street.

"Not today," I answered. "I'm in a hurry."

The truth was that I saw three M.P.'s drawing close so
I didn't want to stop. It was the first time I had not bought
a bag of hot chestnuts from Old Man Fan when I met him.
As I reached the southern part of Tiger Street, the M.P.'s
who had been trailing me finally called me to a halt. They
surrounded me.

"Your pass?" the first M.P. demanded.

I showed it to him. As I was doing so, the second M.P.
tried to snatch one of the money bundles. I held on tightly
and when I would not let go, he said:

"This American devil values his money."

The third M.P. said sullenly: "We don't want your
money! You're a capitalist! You would die to save your
money!"

He was right this time! I would have held on to it even
if it had meant death. It was a game they were playing.
I was the rat — and they were the cats. They would be delighted to see me cringe. The three M.P.'s leered at me,
showing their surprise that I was unyielding.

Then the first M.P. asked: "What do you think of our
great leader, Mao?"

I didn't want to reply, but they pressed me.

"Great man," I replied ironically.

"Is he greater than Lincoln?"

In my resentment I became sarcastic. "Of course Mao
Tse-Tung is greater. Has he not liberated 450,000,000
people?"

The first M.P. sensed my inference, but he only leered

and moved on. The other two M.P.'s followed him in the performance of their duty. Why didn't they turn on me? They knew the truth, but like the 450,000,000, they were also in the Red net — trapped like poor fish.

I hurried on and at last saw the gates of our Mission. They looked like the gates of Paradise! They were open and I walked through. Then I rushed through the courtyard and headed straight for Father Kent's room. Oh, to see a friendly face! To be able to say exactly what I thought!

"Thank God I'm home," I shouted. "I've just come out of Hell!"

Even the thought that we now had enough money to pay our bills gave me no comfort. How gladly would I have forfeited every cent we had could I have brought back the old Dragon Town I loved!

8

An Interlude in the Attic

FATHER KENT held up a razor blade as I came into the room. He had been using it on a thick book that lay open before him on the desk.

"This sharp instrument and my energy," Father Kent orated, "are dedicated to the great purpose that your sojourn on earth may be extended to a hundred years of happy life with your devoted Chinese!"

"Oh, Frank," I asked impatiently, "what are you doing? This is no time for riddles!"

"Why, John, I'm saving your life for your great and noble purpose," he answered with a grin. I could tell from his dramatics that he was trying to distract me from my worries.

"What is the book that is sharpening your wits and dulling your razor?" I asked.

Father Kent lifted the page he had expurgated from the book and, leaning back to observe my reaction, he passed it to me. I saw that it was our teachers' manual, used to explain Christian doctrine. Halfway down the

printed page I came upon a heavily underlined sentence.
I read it aloud:

" 'Communism is the enemy of the Lord of Heaven. Religion, and every friend of Religion, must fight against
it.' "

"There, indeed, is the damning evidence to hang us
from the ancient camphor tree in the public park," Father
Kent declared. "The Reds, it is rumored, hang their
enemies by their thumbs. Your little thumbs and mine
would certainly feel the terrible strain."

He sized me up, then drew up his own powerful frame.
"I'm only 180 pounds. It wouldn't be so hard for me as
for you. But to expurgate the books is easier for both of us
than hanging and not half so disgraceful."

The policy Kent and I had worked out after many serious discussions was to avoid making trouble or irritating
the Reds unnecessarily. Our stand against them — when
and if it came — would be in defense of our principles.

"My," I shouted, slapping my forehead, "we have two
thousand teachers' manuals in the attic!"

"I know it," Father Kent said. "And with so many, Captain Fu could easily accuse us of subversive activities. It
might be just the chance he's looking for."

"How did you happen to remember these?" I asked.

"I was preparing a sermon, and as I was looking up a
point I opened the book to that sentence," Father Kent
explained. "Then Young Ma came in. I showed it to him
and he pointed out that even if there were only a few
copies around the Mission, it would be bad enough. But
to have two thousand volumes hidden in the attic! If the
Reds found them they would suspect we were ready to
spread propaganda against them at the first opportunity."

"What do you propose?" I asked Father Kent.

"Deletion is better than hanging. So Young Ma and I, with your permission, would like to climb up into the attic after dark and cut out the incriminating evidence. Flip the pages and you'll see how difficult it is to detect that missing page!"

At seven o'clock that evening, Young Ma came into the library and reported that he had completed the registration for Captain Fu. I wanted to tell him that I had seen Li Li Pan on my trip to the People's Bank, but I decided to wait for a more favorable opportunity. I knew that Father Kent was anxious to get started on the work of deleting the page from the two thousand teachers' manuals stacked in the attic.

"Let's begin 'Operation Expurgation,'" Father Kent urged.

At the word "begin," Young Ma got the stepladder from the corridor and brought it into the library. He placed it directly under the ceiling trapdoor, climbed up the ladder, opened the trapdoor and lifted himself up into the attic with ease. Father Kent followed. He was heavy, and the stepladder squeaked under his weight. I held it steady and Young Ma gave him a hand. When he reached the top step, he was not quite able to lift himself through the opening. I pushed from below, and Young Ma pulled from above; finally, Father Kent disappeared into the attic.

I removed my cassock, and rolled up my shirt sleeves. I got a blue cap from my room and decided to join them in the attic to participate in "Operation Expurgation."

I started up the stepladder and with each ascending step I took, the ladder creaked. When I reached the top rung it cracked, and I felt as if it were collapsing under me. Father Kent and Young Ma, both grinning, reached down from the trapdoor to steady me. My corpulence seemed an obstacle to further progress.

My situation and appearance struck Kent as comical. "Where do you think you're going?" He laughed. I felt like a fat man poised to chin himself on a bar, waiting hopefully for the power of levitation to assist him in the achievement. There I was on the top of the stepladder and helpless. But I was determined to get into the attic and do my part.

"Will this small attic hold the three of us?" Father Kent asked. "Suppose it should collapse, and all of us land with a crash in the library with two thousand teachers' manuals on top of us? Suppose Captain Fu should appear on the scene of the catastrophe while we are in that deplorable state? I ask you, don't you think he would suspect us of having been engaged in espionage? And our 'Operation Expurgation' would be a complete failure!"

I was forced to listen to his oratorical plea, but I insisted that I must join them. Finally, I managed to crawl into the attic. The three of us were perspiring.

Father Kent puffed: "We should have had a derrick for hoisting."

The attic was so low that we had to stoop even in the center. I had to drop on my hands and knees to maneuver on the sides of the attic where the manuals were stacked. By candlelight, I pulled the stacks, in bundles of ten volumes, to the center.

Father Kent and Young Ma squatted with bent heads as they cut out the incriminating pages. My task was to supply my industrious companions with books. In the candlelight, as I lay prostrate, I watched the other two silently perform their part.

Suddenly I detested what we were doing. We were not spies! Why should we be sneaking on our hands and knees in the attic? We were honest men, I thought to myself. Why are we, by candlelight, after dark, in the attic, acting like spies? I was helpless and aggravated, but I didn't dare interrupt my good companions who, with nimble hands, were rapidly cutting out the condemning pages from the books.

Then I began to feel pains in my back and knees as I wriggled and strained to bring out the bundles. I was not accustomed to this mode of locomotion! I lay flat on my stomach and stretched myself to my full length. What a relief! In that posture, I observed that Father Kent had paused to rub his legs which had fallen asleep.

He said: "My legs feel like they've been amputated."

He, too, was trying to stretch himself. Young Ma, however, did not stir. His fine hands flew over the pages as he skillfully manipulated the razor blade. He showed no signs of pain or fatigue. How ashamed I was of myself! I was too soft!

"Who on earth decided to order two thousand of these manuals?" I asked Father Kent.

"You did, of course, John," Father Kent retorted.

"If you hadn't persuaded me to accompany you to the bookshop, I wouldn't have been influenced to buy so many!" I answered heatedly. "You painted a rosy world — the Reds would never get to Dragon Town — not for at least ten years. The convert movement would be on a large scale. You were an optimist, Frank. You should have seen into the future and known we'd come to this — expurgating on a large scale in a low attic, cramped like sardines."

I must confess, however, that Father Kent was right about converts. If the Reds hadn't come so soon, the manuals would have been used up within a year.

When we had gone through a thousand books, I proposed that we leave the attic and have a cup of tea. My companions wouldn't hear of it.

"How would we ever get you up here again?" Father Kent laughingly asked.

Sadly realizing the truth of this, I gritted my teeth, and followed the steadfast example of my companions. I forgot myself for a while as I contemplated the endurance of Young Ma. He was in an unenviable position. Captain Fu would certainly continue to hound him. He had been jilted by Li Li Pan, and there is no pain equal to the pain of love.

How beautiful Li Li Pan had looked in the vegetable garden. Her beauty was a joy to behold, even in the drab uniform of the Red Army, I thought. I began to feel that I would be willing to subject myself to worse tortures than the cramped attic if I could save Young Ma from Captain Fu and win Li Li Pan from the Communist cause. I felt heroic just meditating upon it. Occupied as I was with my thoughts, I only moaned occasionally although my back was breaking.

I had to talk! I told Young Ma I had seen Li Li Pan with the students. He paused a moment when I said "Li Li Pan," and although his expression didn't change, I sensed that he was glad to hear her name mentioned.

"When did you see her last?" I asked Young Ma.

He hesitated, but I knew he was pleased to have a

chance to unburden himself. Working as he talked, he said:

"Father, the late edition of the *Red North Star* had a front-page article by Li Li Pan, with her picture, condemning her parents. Her parents have been put in jail. She wrote: 'They deserve to be punished for oppressing the poor people.' She praised the People's Government for confiscating their land and dividing it among the poor."

"Why is she so bitter toward her parents?" I asked.

"It is resentment, Father," Young Ma answered. "She wished to flee to Hongkong before liberation, but Mr. Pan would not agree. He thought that he had sufficient power in Dragon Town to save his interests. His underground friends had promised him that the Reds would treat him fairly, and employ him in the People's Government. All this he believed. Li Li Pan had urged that they run away, so now that her parents are trapped, she has denounced them publicly to save herself." Then Young Ma added: "Father, life is sweet."

"Does she know your background?"

"Yes, Father. I once told her my whole life story."

"Do you think she will denounce you, too?" I inquired.

"That is something only the future will tell, Father," Young Ma said. "She knows that I never will become a Communist; that my family has been Catholic for the past hundred years; that my father died at the hands of the Reds; and that I feel it deeply. She also knows that I am stubborn and unyielding."

I looked at Ma's powerful athletic figure, his sure, delicate hands at work; I thought of the valiant warrior! We all worked on in silence. Though my unused muscles had me on the rack, I no longer rebelled at the pain. It seemed to bring me closer to my noble, patient friends.

It was twelve o'clock when the irksome task, "Operation Expurgation," was completed. As the new day began, Young Ma cut the last page out of the final copy of the teachers' manual! Wearily we stumbled to the ladder. Suddenly a loud gonglike noise burst through the stillness. We froze. Could we be discovered? Then I heard a laugh from Father Kent — low at first, but growing louder till it was the jolly roar I so often enjoyed. He bent down, then lifted his arms and swung them together over his head. Another clang — not quite so loud this time.

"Look, John, at what I've found! This is the way to get us in trim so we'll be able to climb up to the attic easily!"

Ma Chung and I craned our necks to see. "These are my horseshoes from home!" he said proudly. "Did you know your humble assistant was once a champ? I haven't thrown a horseshoe in the past ten years — our missionary life kept me too busy! But now that our captain friends won't let us out of the compound, you and I will bring a great new sport to Dragon Town. When we're through, you'll have no trouble climbing up to the attic, if we ever have to go through another session like tonight's."

Tired as I was that night, I didn't realize what a relaxation and comfort Father Kent's discovery of the horseshoes would be in the trying days ahead. Again and again they served as useful allies in helping me regain my balance after the pressure of a workout in the "Red ring!"

9

Ting Hao for Father Kent

FATHER KENT did not waste any time in putting his discovery into action. The next day was clear and mild; after lunch he handed the horseshoes to me while he went to the woodshed.

Su Li was sitting on the steps watching the soldiers at drill, but the ever-curious lad immediately came running to find out what we were going to do now. "What have you got?" he asked, pointing to the irons.

"Horseshoes," I said, tossing him one.

"What are the holes for, Father?" He ran his hands around the curves, poking his fingers through the slots.

"To nail the iron shoe on the horse's hoof," I explained.

"But you haven't got a horse!"

"I won't need one, Su Li. Father Kent and I will play a game."

Su Li gaped at me in puzzlement. "How can you play a game with these irons, Father?" he asked, wide-eyed. Luckily, Father Kent came out just then carrying the iron rods and the sledge hammer — saving me from **Su Li's** million questions.

"Come on," Father Kent said. "I'll show you."

Su Li no longer had an interest in the soldiers' activities. He was fascinated by the horseshoe that he still held in his hand.

Father Kent led the way past the turkey's pen. As usual a group of soldiers were standing around. The turkey was putting on a fine show. He had his colorful feathers spread out, fan wise, and was strutting with all the dignity of a drum major. The soldiers admired his performance and imitated his stride, swinging their arms, and holding their heads high, mimicking the turkey's "gobble, gobble, gobble" sound.

In a workmanlike way Father Kent chose a clear space and set one of the rods in the ground. I held it as he hammered the spike down firmly. The clang of iron attracted the attention of the soldiers quartered in the houses of our neighbors.

"Look!" shouted one to his comrades. "That boy has a horseshoe in his hands!" In their northern province horses were common. The soldiers turned their backs on the proud turkey and ran over to Su Li. They passed the horseshoe among them, feeling and examining it.

One soldier said wonderingly, "It is very large!"

Su Li explained importantly: "They were made in America." At the word "America," the soldiers at once frowned, and returned the iron shoe to Su Li.

As we finished driving in the first spike I looked up and saw soldiers watching us not only on the ground but on the wall. By the time we had driven both rods into the ground the whole north and south walls of the Mission were covered with soldiers. They watched, but made no remark. Their very silence made me nervous. If they would only open their mouths, they would seem more human!

"I don't like all these soldiers staring at us from the walls of the Mission property," I said to Father Kent. "We may run into trouble."

"Come, John, the soldiers need distraction, too, from their daily routine," Father Kent answered. "Let's entertain them by pitching a good game of horseshoes. Hold the shoe this way, John. Now throw it." I did, but it wobbled in the air and landed on its side, rolling near Su Li.

Father Kent threw a shoe. It turned evenly through the air in circles, bumped in front of the iron stake and slipped on to it with a clink. It was a "ringer!"

Su Li jumped up and down, clapped his hands and shouted: "The horseshoe is around the iron rod. *Ting hao,* very good, Father!"

I looked at the soldiers standing near. They stood stiff, like poles, a sullen expression on their faces. I glanced at the soldiers on the wall; they looked like a hundred dummies with sour faces.

"Relax, John," Father Kent demanded. "Stop looking up at the soldiers. I'll make a champion horseshoe thrower out of you if you concentrate a little."

"Just as you say, Frank." I kept getting closer to the stake with each throw, and I became so engrossed in the game that I forgot about the Red spectators. Father Kent threw ringers frequently, which made Su Li happy. As Su Li picked up the shoes he said to me, "Not bad, Father," and to Father Kent he kept repeating gleefully, *"Ting hao,* very good."

"You know, John, I've played this game for a long time," Father Kent said, as we walked back and forth from the stakes. "I was eight years old when I first began pitching horseshoes on the farm with my father. He was the champion of La Grange, Iowa, and he was very proud of his title. In the spring, when the weather was good, he would have me out in our yard practicing. We had horseshoe contests in both grammar and high school and I was always on the winning team. My father hoped that I would be a champion one day.

"In high school, a missioner from China gave us a talk on vocations. After the talk, we had recreation. It was spring, and since horseshoe pitching was very popular in La Grange, we had a dozen pitching ranges. The China missioner came over to where I was playing. He began pitching, and he was good. He made three ringers in a row. While we pitched horseshoes, he told me about Maryknoll. Out of our mutual liking for the game, a friendship grew. He took my name, and when he returned to China he wrote me twice a year.

"In my fourth year of high school, while we were playing a game, my father asked me what I thought I'd do after graduation. I didn't answer him at once. 'Do you want to go to Notre Dame?' he asked me.

"Many times I had heard my father say to my mother, 'Frank is going to Notre Dame to college.' He admired Notre Dame very much. I hated to disappoint him, but I said, 'No.'

"My father's face dropped when he heard my negative reply.

"'Father,' I said, 'I want to go to China.' He looked surprised.

"'How are you going to do that, son?' he asked. 'Join the Marines?'

"I smiled. 'That's one way of getting there, but what I want to do is go to Maryknoll.' As I told him that, I threw a horseshoe and dropped a ringer."

"Well, Frank, you've made lots of ringers at your work in China, even if you never tossed a horseshoe here until today. And I suppose La Grange will be proud of you, when they hear you were hung by the Chinese Reds?" Somehow, I couldn't help trying to ruffle the calm with which he took all our trials!

"There you go, John, bringing up unpleasant subjects just when I'm enjoying myself! Go ahead and see if you can get your horseshoe to land anywhere near the rod!"

I tossed the shoe carelessly — I'd just about given up hope, for this time anyway.

"Ting hao," called Su Li excitedly from the rod. "You finally made it, Father Roman. You got a ringer, too!"

10
Captain Sun Borrows
a Radio

FATHER KENT sat at the
portable organ in the library
that evening playing "Carry
Me Back to Old Virginny." I watched as his large hands
rhythmically rose and fell on the keys — a performance
that always fascinated me. Some evenings Kent tried to
teach me to play, but I preferred to listen to him. This
evening I relaxed, enjoying the plaintive music of the Old
South of far-off America. Glancing across the room, I was
suddenly shocked to alertness.

As my eyes turned to the door they encountered five
Red soldiers standing there, motionless and silent. All
were carrying guns.

I recognized Captain Sun, the Red officer with the
rough face and the malicious, beady eyes.

This was the first time the Red soldiers had entered the
rectory unannounced. I was startled — and annoyed because Su Wen had not come to warn me of their arrival.

While I struggled with myself to receive the night visitors pleasantly, Father Kent remained seated unconcernedly at the organ and played on as if it were a common thing to have soldiers present as his musical audience. His nonchalant attitude encouraged me and I tried to imitate him; I pretended that I was glad to see them.

"Please come in and sit down," I said, like a genial host. Captain Sun responded to my invitation by placing his hand on his holster. Soft strains of music filled the room. I carried out the Oriental ritual of offering the guests tea and cigarettes; Captain Sun returned my hospitality with a leer.

Since the captain and his comrades refused to enter the library, I asked Captain Sun what the purpose of his visit was. He then stepped forward, with his hand still resting on his holster, and said:

"I have come to borrow your radio."

From his hostile attitude I had received the impression that he had come to arrest us. I was relieved when he made known his request. I looked toward Father Kent for guidance. He still had his back turned toward me and seemed so intent on his music that when I called: "Frank," he pretended not to hear me. Instead, he bent forward and pumped the pedals faster in order to increase the volume of his music. Was that his signal to advise me to keep calm and refuse the radio?

"Captain," I said cordially, "you are welcome to listen to the radio in the parlor."

He replied firmly: "I have come to *borrow* the radio."

Trying to stall, I remarked: "It is necessary to have indirect electric current to operate the radio. Do you have a transformer?"

He snapped back: "Yes!"

The expression on his face, however, showed that he did not understand what I meant.

"Let us go to the parlor," I said, "and I'll show you what I mean."

"I have come for the radio!" he repeated loudly.

"Of course," I answered, and with that I stepped out into the corridor. Two soldiers lined up in front of me, the other three behind; in that formation we walked into the parlor. I felt as if I were a criminal being led to jail.

My departure from the library was accompanied by Father Kent's soft music. Why didn't Kent stop playing the organ and come to see what was happening to me? Did he think that his melodious music was soothing the savage breast of Captain Sun? As I asked myself these questions, I accidentally brushed against Captain Sun's revolver. The cold steel sent a shiver up my spine. We entered the parlor and I stepped up to the radio.

"See this box?" I said to Captain Sun. "Without it, the radio won't work!" I pointed to the transformer.

He inspected it and answered that the Signal Corps had one. At the mention of the Signal Corps it occurred to me that perhaps Captain Sun was not entirely ignorant about radios.

"Disconnect it quickly," he said sharply.

"But I must show you how to operate it first," I remarked.

I hated to see the radio leave the rectory. If Captain Sun took it away, he would never bring it back. I had heard that the Reds would eventually require an inventory of everything in the rectory. If the radio was missing, they would accuse me of having sent it to the Nationalist guerrillas who were holding out against them in the mountains to the west of Dragon Town, and I feared that I might become politically involved. Nevertheless, with Captain Sun standing over me, I began to loosen the wires from the transformer.

I asked the captain, "Will you give me a receipt?"

He didn't answer; I stopped working. If I am going to get into trouble over this radio, I thought, it might as well happen now! Captain Sun put his hand to his holster once again but I didn't stir. I even became daring; I went so far as to join the wires I had disconnected!

"All Communist soldiers observe the laws of the Red Army!" he yelled at me. "Borrow something — give a receipt!"

"Since that is so, Captain Sun, will you kindly make out the receipt for the radio?"

He called for a piece of paper, and drew a fountain pen from his coat pocket. Then he hurriedly scribbled the receipt and stamped it with his seal.

"Quick," he shouted in an angry voice, "disconnect that radio! Carry it to the kitchen! There you can explain how to operate it!"

The captain seemed anxious to get out of the rectory. It struck me that he felt out of bounds. There was something about the rectory of American priests that made him uncomfortable.

I did as I was told. I detached the radio from the various wires and carried it to the kitchen. The kitchen was a separate, small, low brick building and was located on the right side of the Mission grounds. It was connected to the rectory by a covered walk.

I was surprised to find Su Wen there baking bread.

Since he had not appeared when the soldiers first arrived, I had presumed that he had gone to a meeting at the north end of Tiger Street. I was puzzled by his attitude when I entered carrying the radio and attended by five armed soldiers. He showed no sign of bewilderment but looked on without saying a word.

I placed the radio on a table, and plugged it into a wall socket, then began to explain how to tune in the different broadcasting stations. It was turned on to Peiping, when all of a sudden the electric light in the kitchen went out. The radio stopped playing, and we were all enveloped in complete darkness!

I heard the soldiers draw their guns from their holsters and felt their breath on my neck. They were standing that close to me! I expected them to grasp my arms, but they did not touch me at all. Were they suspicious that, since I was an "American foreign devil," I possessed a magic power to harm them?

The sudden darkness no doubt had astounded them. I knew I had blown a fuse unintentionally, but how was I to explain that to Captain Sun? I shuddered, and made an act of contrition. I was certain I would face my Lord and Judge that very night. But strangely enough the darkness affected us like a spell. We all stood quite still.

"Please excuse me," Su Wen began in a soft, apologetic tone. "My fault. Loose wire. Happens often. Forgive me, I will light a candle. I have one here on the shelf. Always keep it ready for emergency. I am an unworthy man. Sorry to cause trouble."

His appealing and convincing staccato phrases were accompanied by his rapid movements. He lit the candle and changed the fuse in the switch box. As the kitchen light came on, he stopped talking and bowed humbly. Then he returned to his place at the kitchen table.

What a perfect actor!

The radio lit up and then gave forth a hum. I was glad it wasn't burned out. In a second Chinese music came over the airwaves from the Peiping broadcasting station. I took one glance at my visitors and shut my eyes; five guns were trained on me! I marveled at the fact that I was still alive! The revolvers disappeared into their holsters, and I breathed more easily.

Captain Sun yelled excitedly: "Let us get out of this foreign devil's place at once!"

I hastily pulled out the plug and wrapped the wires around the radio. The captain put it under his arm and departed with his comrades at his heels, leaving me with the receipt clutched in my hand.

"You saved my life!" I said gratefully to Su Wen. He was covering the dough with a woollen blanket so that it would rise by early morning when he would bake it in the kitchen stove. I felt as if I had been in the jaws of death and had been miraculously rescued.

Su Wen looked at me and said: "Trouble, Father. Bird of Sorrow come. But, Father, keep bird out of hair!"

I entered my room and prepared for bed, but I was again too restless to go to sleep. I sat in the rocking chair and picked up a book of poetry. Gradually I lulled myself to sleep. The last line I had in my mind was: "When fishes flew, and birds talked, and the moon was blue, I was born." My world, I said to myself while half-asleep, surely made less sense than the poetry I was reading!

I dozed in the rocking chair, and dreamed that a blue bird was tapping at my window. The tapping persisted and awakened me. It turned out to be a lively knock at the windowpane of my room.

"Father — wake up!" I heard the familiar voice of Su Wen say. "You are wanted," he continued, his voice urgent. "Open the door. I have been calling you for the past quarter-hour. Hurry! Captain Sun is furious!"

Since I was already dressed, I paused only long enough to grab my hat and coat. It was midnight, and I wanted to be warmly dressed if I was going somewhere with the captain. Again my premonition that I would be taken to jail in the dead of night! I opened the door to find Captain Sun standing there with the radio under his arm, his four comrades directly behind him.

"I am returning the radio to you tonight," he announced mockingly. "You were so reluctant to let me have it that you must have a great need for it!"

He passed the radio over to me. Then he and his comrades departed in silence.

As I closed the front door, I heard their snickers. I examined the radio. It smelled of burned rubber. I could tell at once that the radio was out of order. I'd never be able to get it fixed!

The Bird of Sorrow descended on my head and nested in my black hair. I took him to bed with me for I was too discouraged to shoo him away.

11

Su Li and the Honorable Monkey Ancestors

A GOOD SLEEP, a beautiful morning, and the spirit of hope all combined to dislodge the Bird of Sorrow from my hair.

Early next day I walked out into the courtyard where I stopped beside the flower bed along the Mission wall to admire the yellow chrysanthemums, shaped like large buttons, in full bloom. These were the last of the autumn season, and in the morning sun they looked glorious. I looked around the courtyard with pleasure.

In accordance with Chinese tradition, St. Joseph's Mission was enclosed by a high brick wall. The enclosure was called a compound. The church was on the right. On the left were Su Wen's house, the common kitchen, the house of Young Ma and the rectory kitchen.

Between the church and the living quarters of Su Wen and Ma there was a spacious courtyard behind which was the rectory. It was a one-story brick building, rectangular

in shape. The length of it faced the main entrance on
Tiger Street. The gate had a plain, double-leaved door
constructed of thick planks fastened by two wooden bolts.
It stood wide open to the road. In fact, the gate was never
closed any more, not even at night.

The back of our Mission was on the bank of the Fu
River. The back wall also had a small gate but it was always kept closed except when Su Wen drew water from the
river in wooden buckets.

The beauty of the day lifted my spirits higher and I
moved from the yellow chrysanthemums to a rosebush.
Two red roses were in full bloom. The beautiful
rose petals, I reflected, would wither and fall, but the rosebush would flourish on through the most trying condi-
tions; neither frost nor near-freezing weather nor heavy
rains could kill it. I recalled that years ago, when I first
came to China, I was told the history of this very rosebush
by the French missionary, Father Laval.

When I first met Father Laval, he was eighty years old;
his hair was snow white, his narrow face was full of
wrinkles, he had a grayish flowing beard. He was thin and
had the stoop of old age. That had been twenty-five years
ago, when I was young. Father Laval had since died in
Canton.

I remember that Father Laval had said that the rosebush, which I was looking at this very moment, was a
shoot from a rosebush brought from France and planted
in Canton, Kwangtung Province. A shoot from the Canton
rosebush was planted in Wuchow, Kwangsi Province (a
city a hundred miles from Canton), by Father Heron. A
cutting from the Wuchow rosebush was planted in Nanning, the capital of Kwangsi Province, five hundred miles

west of Canton. From the Nanning rosebush a cutting was made and brought to Dragon Town, two hundred miles northwest of Canton in Kwangsi Province, South China, by Father Rigal. All of these valiant French Fathers had now passed on to their eternal reward.

Would I be left much longer to protect the flowers they had planted? What chance, I thought, would a red rose have of living in this Communist state — where everything existed solely to contribute to the power of the People's Government?

I looked out the open gate. No longer did we have the privilege of going out into Dragon Town. Even if I had been allowed, how could I venture out into a world so completely changed?

As I gazed out at Tiger Street, I saw a squad of soldiers tramp by. They were going through their military drill. Their cloth shoes shuffled on the dirt street; the challenge of the guards sounded from the compounds to the right and left of the Mission. Liso's compound to the right was occupied by a general, and Li's compound to the left was being used by a propaganda unit of the military security police. An empty lot across the street had been transformed into a basketball court; I saw soldiers running back and forth, but the baskets were not visible. I heard the rattle of the donkey carts and the rumble of our confiscated jeep. It passed by loaded with brown paper cartons — some sort of supplies. Then I heard the boisterous laughter of boys in the street. How strange! Then the running patter of many feet.

I waited tensely to see which boys would pass the Mission gate. Who dared to laugh so heartily? In a moment a group of small boys dressed in blue uniforms stopped in front of the Mission gate. They were out of breath from running, but they were grinning. Something hilarious had happened, I surmised. In the group of ten boys I saw Su Li. His schoolmates shouted:

"See you after breakfast."

"I'll be waiting for you," Su Li answered.

His schoolmates ran off toward the north end of Tiger Street, each to his respective home for morning rice. Su Li, bubbling with mirth and still grinning, entered the courtyard. He saw me standing near the flower bed.

"God bless you, Father," he said cheerfully.

How big Su Li was getting for his age — he was only ten. His round, full face was like the moon and his wide mouth was always ready to eat or smile. His black slanted eyes were more inquisitive than nine cats. He was talkative, too — that was a characteristic he had inherited from his progenitor.

Fishing and boats interested him more than books although he always made good grades in school. His father wanted him to be a scholar and grumbled when he saw his son fishing with a bamboo pole from the banks of the Fu.

This morning Su Li was wearing a trim blue uniform and a cap. This was something new. I had never seen him wear a cap before and I had known him since he was a baby.

"You look wonderful all dressed up in your new clothes, Su Li," I said.

"Father, this uniform and cap are now the regulation at school," he replied.

"What was all the laughter about?" I asked. "You and your schoolmates were hilarious!"

"Oh, Father," he asked excitedly, "do I look like a monkey?"

I was astounded at this unexpected query. Before I could answer, Su Li was down on his hands awkwardly imitating a monkey by leaping around and making a squealing sound. Simultaneously he extended a hand as if in the act of begging for peanuts.

I was astonished but I laughed heartily. Then I heard the words: "You stupid wonder!" come from the kitchen door. It was the strong voice of Su Li's father, Su Wen. Shocked at the pranks of his illustrious son, he bellowed again:

"Get up, you little devil! Are you going out of your mind playing in that manner and in your new suit? Do you think I print money like the government?"

At his father's sharp command, Su Li stood up smiling and satisfied. He asked: "Do you like my monkey act, Father?"

"Pretty good, boy," I replied, still in the dark as to what had inspired him. Teasingly I added: "Su Li, you're too fat. You eat too many cookies to be agile like a monkey. Why the sudden enthusiasm about monkeys anyhow?"

"Father, school opened today," Su Li announced.

I nodded, remembering that classes had been resumed for the first time today since the People's Liberation Army evacuated the Chin Lung, Golden Dragon School, three days previously.

"This morning on my way to school with my classmates," went on Su Li, "we saw several soldiers playing with a monkey at the corner of Tiger and Lion streets. They were in front of Madame Wu's candy shop."

"But aren't monkeys rare?" I asked.

"Oh, yes, Father. My eyes popped! I'd heard of monkeys and I'd seen pictures of them in books, but this was the first time I saw a real live one. Father, I couldn't stop looking at it. I would have stared at that queer creature all day but the school gong rang, and one of the soldiers chased us off to school, shouting: 'You little devils! I don't want the monkey to get into trouble with your teachers.' I ran across the street with the other boys, trying to imitate the monkey, until I got into the classroom."

"Seeing a monkey for the first time, Su Li, you've become monkey-minded," I declared, with a laugh.

"I guess I wouldn't have remembered it so well, Father, but the first lesson we had today provoked reflections on monkeys."

"You're speaking like a scholar, Su Li," I said. "I don't understand you."

"Well, Father, I am now in the seventh grade, you know, and we have a new teacher. His name is Hao. He's very tall and comes from North China. He told the class that the Golden Dragon School is now called the Eighth District Liberation School. 'Liberation is what China needs,' Teacher Hao told us, 'and you boys must assist in the achievement of this great goal.' After his speech he gave out new books to the class." Su Li, pulling his copy out of his coat pocket, asked: "Want to see mine, Father?"

I took it. The title on the cover read: *The New Order of the People's Cultural Foundations.* Beneath there was a portrait of Mao Tse-Tung, the leader of the Chinese People's Republic. He was dressed in a plain uniform.

I was curious to thumb through the pages, but I was more curious to hear Su Li's story, so I asked him: "Where do the monkeys come in?"

"Teacher Hao began to explain the first lesson," Su Li answered. "As he was talking, I was watching a bird on the window sill. But then I heard him say: 'Our ancestors come from monkeys.' Monkeys! I said to myself. I have just seen the way they act! I began listening hard and then I started to think of monkeys and of how silly the monkey I'd seen had acted. When I thought of him as my ancestor I began to smile, then I snickered, and finally I broke out into a loud laugh. I tried to control myself because I had upset the class, but the thought of monkeys and ancestors struck me so funny that instead of quieting down, I became boisterous. The whole class got into an uproar and I was to blame. I stopped laughing then because I was embarrassed and frightened, too, at the way I had disrupted the class. I thought I would be punished and I was scared. I hadn't meant any harm, but how could I prove that to the teacher? I was so worried I began to cry.

" 'What is comical about monkey ancestors?' Teacher Hao asked the whole class in a quiet voice. He didn't sound angry. 'Su Li, stand up,' he said calmly, 'and explain your hilarity.' I trembled as I stood up, and hung my head; I didn't dare open my mouth. 'Speak up, comrade Su Li,' he said kindly. This was the first time he had called anybody 'comrade.' 'In the New China, a pupil is permitted to speak his mind in class. Freedom of speech is a basic principle in our schools.' Some of the boys sitting close to me whispered: 'Su Li, tell him.'

"In a timid tone I declared: 'This morning was the first time I saw a real live monkey. A soldier had one at the end of an iron chain. This monkey was so hairy, with no chin, and his ears stuck out, and he had a long tail. He acted so foolishly and looked so queer, and when I heard you say . . .' I stopped there, for I was afraid to go on. Teacher Hao patiently interposed: 'Comrade Su Li, continue. Remember, freedom of speech.'

"I told him that our ancestors were dignified and important people, and comparing them with monkeys struck me as very funny. Father, I began to shake, for the whole class started to laugh all over again. I was sure that through no fault of my own I was doomed.

"To my surprise, Teacher Hao merely remarked: 'I readily understand that you poor boys have been raised in the darkness of the ancient classics and have no new scientific knowledge of the world. I am here to guide you by the light of the New Order in China. Of course, brainwashing will cleanse your minds.' Then he announced: 'Class is dismissed for the morning.' I was too scared about what would happen to me to listen to what he said. I thought my punishment would be some sort of washing. Again to my surprise I was dismissed with my class.

"As I left the classroom, Teacher Hao patted me on the head and said to me: 'Su Li, you're a smart boy.' I was very happy that I had gotten out of trouble so easily and I made up my mind to have nothing to do with monkeys any more. I wanted to be rid of them — like evil spirits."

"But how does it happen that you've changed your resolution?" I inquired. "It seems to me that you're more interested in monkeys now than ever before."

"Well, Father, it's like this," Su Li answered. "After I got out of school I saw a lot of people in front of Madame Wu's candy shop. They were in a circle watching four monkeys that some soldiers were having fun with. At first I was going to keep going, but I was so curious that I joined the circle. I wasn't scared any more so it was fun to see the monkeys imitating the soldiers. As I watched the antics of the monkeys I couldn't understand what they had to do with my ancestors. I began to feel angry with Teacher Hao and his new scientific knowledge. It certainly didn't seem right to me. Since I wasn't afraid any more, I enjoyed the silly performance of the monkeys along with the crowd."

Then he inquired: "Father, do you know Scholar Lee, the little man with the thin silver beard on his chin and the long flowing gown?"

"Of course I do. He is the most learned scholar of ancient China on Tiger Street."

"I noticed that the Venerable Scholar was also watching the funny gestures of the monkeys," Su Li remarked. "I edged myself alongside of him. Since he was a respected sage, I was anxious to ask him about monkey ancestors. I addressed him:

" 'Honorable One, do you believe that our ancestors are descendants of the monkeys?' He answered me sharply, 'Boy, what sort of nonsense are you asking?' and like an actor in a play, in a deep, ringing voice that could be heard above the din of the crowd, he said: 'Our ancestors were great people. History has faithfully recorded their noble deeds.'

"Hearing Venerable Lee speak so, the crowd turned in his direction. 'Honorable One,' I said, 'I was told so by one who speaks with authority.' I purposely didn't mention Teacher Hao's name.

" 'Son,' Scholar Lee began, 'that is a great insult to our country. Our culture is at least three thousand years old and it has influenced every country in the vast continent of Asia. China is expressly called the Middle Kingdom of

the World because her culture is deeply rooted in man's
reason.' The crowd shouted: 'That's right — the sage talks
sense!'

" 'Look at that stupid thing!' Venerable Lee said in
derision as he pointed to one of the monkeys making a
pass at a soldier with his paw. 'No ancestors of mine come
from that line, my boy!' he asserted dramatically, and
then he left. The crowd cheered at his good sense. The
soldiers must have been afraid that their pet monkeys
might cause a riot, because they led them away to their
barracks over on Lion Street.

"I was happy with what Scholar Lee had said. He is the
one who showed me how to hold the brush and copy
characters. I have often heard him tell about the warriors
of ancient China when he taught little boys like me before
we were ready to go to Golden Dragon School. Venerable
Lee spoke so well of our highly-esteemed ancestors that I
decided to ask other people what they thought of monkey
ancestors. That's why I asked you, Father, and why I
acted like I did," Su Li finished.

"Su Li!" my cook shouted from the kitchen door.
"Come! Breakfast is ready!"

"See you later, Father," Su Li cried.

Eating came first with Su Li; I knew this, so I only
said:

"Leave your new book with me for a few minutes."

"Certainly, Father." Su Li waved and ran off.

I stood in the courtyard and turned to the first lesson.
The title was, "The Origin of Man." The lesson read:

"Many, many years ago the world was inhabited by
monkeys. Everywhere there were trees, and the monkeys
lived in them. Long ago, too, one sunny day two monkeys

while swinging in the branches slipped and landed on their hind legs keeping their forepaws in the air. From that time on they rarely put their forepaws down on the ground. They learned to walk erect on their hind legs and to use their forepaws as hands. They carried their food in their uplifted forepaws and gradually began to do many things that a man does today with his hands. After several thousand years they became transformed into men as we know them today."

I wanted to read on, but Su Li came running out of the kitchen door munching a cookie.

"Father," he said, "my book." He was ready to return to school so I gave it back to him without any comment.

Laughing, he seized my arm and confided: "You know, I asked my father whether his ancestors were monkeys and he shouted at me angrily: 'You stupid wonder! Don't come around here popping off new learning such as calling our ancestors monkeys! I'll spank you!' "

I warned Su Li to keep out of trouble, but he shouted back "Freedom." That's what Teacher Hao had said. Two days later I saw Su Li in the courtyard making a banner for a parade. It was the first opportunity I had to talk with him, for Captain Fu had kept me extremely busy.

"Su Li," I remarked, "you seem to have lost all interest in the monkeys."

"Yes, Father, there aren't any more monkeys around Tiger Street."

"How did that happen, Su Li?"

"Well, Father, I meant to come and tell you what happened, but I haven't seen you when you weren't busy. Every time I came to the rectory door, there were soldiers around so I stayed away. It was this way, Father," he repeated. "Two of my classmates and I decided to make a game out of the monkey question. We stood in front of Madame Wu's candy shop and as the people passed we stopped them.

"They didn't think this was strange, because now the People's Government has employed small boys at the street corners to check identification cards. When we stopped them, they thought we were on official business. My two classmates interrogated them while I mimicked a monkey. As the people stared at me my classmates popped the question: 'Do you believe that your ancestors came from monkeys?' Most people — who probably didn't want to get in an argument — smiled and answered: 'We don't know,' and went on quickly.

"We had interrogated about twenty persons and it was funny to see the queer expressions on their faces. We were having a lot of fun with our game. In the end, we had about ten classmates playing it with us. Finally, we decided to interrogate an old soldier whom we saw coming. He was short and he looked like a kind old man. If he had looked stern like most of the soldiers we probably wouldn't have questioned him — but, in fact, he stopped to talk with us.

"Since he was so friendly two of my classmates asked him the question while I performed my monkey act. 'Do you, comrade' — that's how the classmates addressed him — 'believe that your ancestors are descended from monkeys?' His face turned red and he grabbed me by the back of my neck. 'You little devils,' he yelled, 'stop this nonsense! Go home at once.' He let me go, and I ran like a deer. I was so scared that I didn't eat that night, and I was so worried that while I was in bed the old soldier would come to take me away that I couldn't sleep.

"Next morning I went to school the long way around to avoid the houses where the soldiers are quartered. I took Coffin Alley and was so depressed when I saw so many coffins that I was sure that one of them was for me. In the schoolyard, my classmates stayed away from me. It was my fault because I had thought of the monkey game. I kept to myself and when the bell rang I went into my classroom. I was scared to death that Teacher Hao was going to punish me, but he never said anything about my monkey act on Tiger Street.

"After the morning class I came back to the Mission by way of Lion Street. I passed by the soldiers and one of them recognized me. He caught hold of me as I tried to run away. How stupid I was to have come this way! The soldier asked me if my name was Su Li, and I told him that it was, even though I was sure he was going to put me in jail. He shouted, 'So you're the little devil!' I thought he was going to box my ears but instead he cursed me roundly. 'Did you ask the old soldier if he had monkey ancestors?' I thought I'd better tell the truth, so I replied: 'No, I mimicked a monkey.'

"He replied, 'You're a monkey, all right. I should tie you at the end of an iron chain right now. That old soldier is our commanding officer! He was so furious at your behavior that he ordered us to get rid of our monkey pets. Our commanding officer hates monkeys. He tolerated them until then, but when you interrogated him he got so mad that he had us get rid of them that very night.' So that's how it happened, Father," Su Li said solemnly, continuing to make his banner for the victory parade.

I went into the rectory to tell Father Kent the ending of the sensational monkey story. Here was something amusingly different from our usual routine. It would keep us from trying to guess Captain Fu's next move in our regard.

12
I Try to Tie a Quilt

Su Wen came to the library with a blue envelope in his hand.

"Father, a messenger delivered this envelope. I signed for it," he said.

He gave it to me and then returned to the kitchen. I opened it and pulled out a sheet of blue paper. Father Kent was sitting opposite me resting his head in the palm of his big hand, with his elbow on the table. From this restful pose he looked up and asked:

"What does it say?"

"American foreigners," I read aloud, "are requested to appear at police headquarters tomorrow at ten o'clock." It's signed: "People's Government, Police Headquarters, Foreign Affairs Department, West St., Dragon Town."

"Doesn't it say anything else?" Father Kent inquired.

"Not another word," I said.

We went out to the courtyard to ask Young Ma about it. He was out on business for Captain Fu. We called Su Wen from the kitchen. As he stepped out into the courtyard, I noticed that the gobbler was loose.

"Su Li," I called, "the American chicken is out of his pen."

Su Li appeared at the kitchen door with a bowl of rice and a pair of chopsticks in his hands. Seeing our turkey boldly ignoring the Communist edict, he rushed out and shooed the gobbler back to his pen.

"I wonder why we are wanted at police headquarters," I asked Su Wen. "Have you heard any rumors?"

"Nothing, Father," he answered.

"Do you suppose the American chicken has stirred up political trouble?" I suggested.

"It could be," Father Kent said. "After all, it was a gift from Governor Wang." But from the tone of his voice I knew that he thought that my idea was ridiculous.

"Shall I kill the fire chicken?" Su Wen asked. He used the common Chinese name for the American chicken so as not to hurt our feelings.

"That's what Captain Sun demanded," I said. "And it sounds like a good idea. You put the gobbler in the oven and invite the neighbors. We'll have a feast tonight. When I face the officials of the People's Government tomorrow, I can proudly tell them that it provided a great banquet for the people."

I could already smell the delicious aroma of roasting turkey and see the joyous guests arrive for the feast! I turned, however, to my legal adviser, Father Kent, for the nod of assent. He shook his head — the answer was "no." My vision of merriment vanished and I saw myself spending a dull evening in the library reading Chinese poetry. I missed my Chinese friends, and a lonely feeling came over me.

Just then Madame Wu entered the courtyard. "Father,"

she said, with tears in her eyes, "last night after dark the police arrested my grandson, Fen. This morning I went to the police station and took him a pot of soup. I thought he would be feeling cold and miserable because last night he had to sleep without a quilt. The guards at the entrance to the police station took the pot of soup in to him but they refused to let me see him."

Madame Wu's grandson, Fen, had been a Nationalist soldier, discharged two years before. I had given him a small sum of money with which he had established a lucrative little business peddling kerosene from house to house. Out of that income he had been able to support his family of three: two sons and his wife.

"Father," Madame Wu pleaded, "what shall I do?"

Formerly I would have given her advice, but now all I could say was:

"Something will be done." It didn't ring true, however.

Su Wen saw my embarrassment. He added: "Don't worry, Madame Wu. In a few days he will be released from jail. Last night fifty persons were picked up after dark by the police on Tiger Street."

Madame Wu returned to her candy shop after I had offered her my poor sympathy. No wonder the Bird of Sorrow hovered over my head!

I turned to Su Wen. "Su Wen," I said, "for our departure to police headquarters tomorrow kindly prepare two heavy quilts which we will take with us. The nights are cold now."

Father Kent interposed: "John, we'll be back."

"Su Wen," I insisted, "get the quilts ready."

Next morning Father Kent and I were ready for our

trip to police headquarters. This was the first time we had ventured into the streets together since the "liberation" of Dragon Town. It was a bright day and the sun was shining in the courtyard. Dressed in our clerical black suits, we stepped out of the rectory into the sunlight.

"John," Father Kent remarked as he observed me in the morning light, "your worries are wearing you down. Your suit hangs loosely on you and your Roman collar looks large."

"That's good," I said. "Now I won't be called a stuffed imperialist. As my bodily curves are reduced, I'll shrink into a poor thin man and the Reds will consider me a small rice basket and no great obstacle to their economic progress."

A rice basket, in Communist language, is a useless person, and now I was forced to consider myself the most useless person in all of Dragon Town. Father Kent, on the other hand, looked not at all like a rice basket. I had not seen him dressed in a clerical suit in several months, and he made a fine-looking priest, I thought, tall and well-proportioned.

Young Ma and Su Li were in the courtyard waiting for us. Young Ma was in agreement with Su Wen that the officials at police headquarters would not detain us. It was the first time the police had ordered us to appear at headquarters and we, as foreigners, probably would only be interrogated — a routine procedure with the People's Government.

Of course no one could be certain so, although Young Ma had objected to our carrying the quilts, he did not force the issue and made no comment when Su Wen appeared in the courtyard with them. The quilts were made of cotton wadding and were covered with a blue-and-white cloth. Each quilt weighed about six pounds and was neatly wrapped in a yellow canvas cloth, tied with brown cord into a compact bundle.

Su Wen was a master at jobs like these. He was a small man, quick in his movements, a characteristic which distinguished him from other Chinese, most of whom are rather slow. In fact, he had been named "the American Cook" because he was so fast in everything he did. As a cook, he was a great consolation. He always had sufficient food for the table, no matter how many guests showed up at the last minute.

Today Su Wen was dressed in a blue uniform and a cap. He looked a little strange to me for I had never seen him dressed in such a formal fashion before. The People's Government urged the ordinary people to dress plainly and frowned on clothes that brought out a person's individuality.

Su Wen laid at our feet the two yellow bundles that he had carried out of the rectory. He then stepped into the kitchen to fetch a bamboo carrying pole. When he returned from the kitchen, he hung the yellow bundles on each end of the carrying pole, and lifted it up on his shoulder.

Young Ma and Su Li said: "God bless you, Fathers," and we set off.

Su Wen led the way and we followed. Father Kent and I walked alongside each other. I recall the striking group we made — Su Wen in his trim blue uniform, the two yellow-bundled quilts at the ends of the carrying pole; Kent and I in somber black clerical suits.

Tiger Street was quiet. Two soldiers were walking on

the left side. In front of Liao's house three guards were
on duty. Liao was a banker who had fled to Hongkong.
His premises were occupied by the military police.

When we reached Madame Wu's candy shop Su Wen
waited outside while I went inside with Father Kent who
wanted to buy a pack of Flying Machine cigarettes. How
clearly every detail of the store comes back to me. A month
before I would have taken it all for granted. Now it was a
bit of China's past — my past — preserved for me!

The candy shop was a low brick building set on the
street. The interior walls were whitewashed and the ceiling was covered with colored pictures from old copies of
The Saturday Evening Post. On the back wall hung Madame Wu's ancestral tablet. In front of it was a small shelf
on which rested a reddish incense burner in which were
three joss sticks that had been freshly lighted. No doubt
the joss sticks were burning because her grandson was in
jail.

Madame Wu was behind the counter. She was a little
woman; her black hair, neatly tied in a knot at the back
of her small head, was heavily streaked with gray. Her dark
almond eyes were lively and flashed with joy when she
saw us. She wore her usual dark-blue gown.

Behind her on the shelves were at least two dozen Klim
cans. The cans were a golden color, and on each can was
pasted a Chinese label indicating what was inside it. I
read the labels: pepper, dried peas, yellow beans, dried
mushrooms, three grades of tea, dried sweet-potato chips,
cinnamon bark. Father Kent had given Madame Wu the
Klim cans.

On several shelves there were cans of Pet milk. These
were empty and mostly ornamental. In a showcase near

the street there were sticks of peppermint candy. Peppermint candy was Madame Wu's specialty. She made it herself, and since there was a grammar school a half block southward on Lion Street, her candy business flourished.

In the inner part of her small shop, on a flat, narrow table, there were three or four kinds of raw tobacco leaves for sale. At the side of the piles there was a balance scale for weighing them. Behind this table there were two shelves on which several brands of cigarettes were on display: Red Wheel, Brave Soldier, Flying Machine (bearing a picture of an airplane), Iron Horse (bearing a picture of a locomotive and train), and a few others.

To the rear of the shop there were two fifty-gallon drums; one contained peanut oil which the Chinese use for cooking, and the other a mild brand of Chinese rice wine. In Dragon Town this wine was called "Three Flowers" wine because of the bubbles that formed in it when it was poured. It is a common thing to have a little rice wine with a meal. It is cheap and on occasion even poor families make a banquet of a meager meal by drinking wine with it.

Madame Wu's ancestors had moved to Dragon Town from Canton two hundred years before. They had been merchants. She had been born in the south end of Dragon Town. Her Cantonese husband also had been a merchant — a rice dealer — and had died in one of the Japanese bombing raids. She had two sons and a daughter living in Singapore. Her sons were successful businessmen who forwarded her a monthly allowance. They had often pleaded with their mother to move to Singapore.

"How can I live in a strange country?" Madame Wu would reply when, on several occasions, Father Kent tried to persuade her to join her sons. "I'm too old and I want to be buried in China."

Now Madame Wu seemed puzzled at our attire. "Why are you wearing strange clothes?" she questioned.

"We are going to police headquarters."

She glanced out into the street and saw Su Wen standing there on the sidewalk holding the carrying pole with the two yellow bundles at his feet. At once she recognized the bundles as quilts.

"What! Are the police ordering you to jail?" she anxiously inquired.

"Oh, no, Madame Wu," Father Kent assured her. "We are taking quilts as a precaution. I want a pack of Flying Machine cigarettes, Madame Wu."

She slowly got a package from the shelf. "You know, two official shop inspectors came here last night," she said. "They took an inventory of the supplies first. One then said: 'Madame Wu, are you an agent for a foreign country?' I told him, 'I don't understand your language.' He said, 'Excuse me. What I meant to ask you is are you friendly with the Americans at the Mission on this street?' I told them, 'Of course I am. The Fathers are the kindest persons I know in this world.' Then the inspector continued, 'Madame Wu, so they are kind to you. Are these yellow cans from the American foreigners?' I replied, 'They are from the Father.' I don't like the word foreigners."

Madame Wu went on: " 'It is easy to see that they have poisoned your heart,' he told me. I asked him what was wrong with the yellow cans — that I use them as containers. He could read the labels for himself. 'Madame Wu, you should be ashamed to have the ceiling of your shop covered with American pictures.' I told him that the paper is very strong and made a good covering for my ceiling, that it kept the dust from the roof tiles. He told me that it was a poor excuse for propagating the false greatness of America to ordinary people.

" 'You are old, Madame Wu, you don't understand the cunning of the American foreigners. I advise you, in the next few days, to get rid of the American cans, and I give you a month to replace the American-papered ceiling with coarse Chinese paper. Even though you are old, and not held responsible for what you do, we still must make an effort to help you change your manner of thinking so that you may also see through the falseness of the foreign devils.'

"Having completed the inventory, the two official inspectors departed. I was so angry, Fathers, that I couldn't talk. I had lost my tongue, I was so taken by surprise at their behavior."

Madame Wu refused to take Father Kent's money for the package of cigarettes and she put several pieces of peppermint candy in a small brown paper bag and gave it to me.

"Father," she said affectionately, "if I do not see you return this afternoon and the police keep you in jail, I will bring you a pot of chicken soup every day."

"You are ten thousand times very kind, Madame Wu," Father Kent said.

"Make rice gruel, Madame Wu," I added, "chicken soup is too expensive."

"Nothing is too good for the Fathers," she responded. (Had the official inspectors heard this remark they would have been absolutely certain that her mind and her heart had been contaminated by the foreign devils!)

How like the Old China I knew — to hear her speak

these kind words! In the new Communist world, where one felt increasingly unwanted, friendship became more valuable than gold.

We went out into Tiger Street. Su Wen swung the carrying pole on his shoulders and the yellow bundles containing the quilts dangled freely. We followed him as he entered Lion Street, which was paved and also had sidewalks. This street was fairly prosperous; both sides were lined with small shops. Usually, Lion Street was noisy but today, at nine o'clock in the morning, it was very quiet and the shops were empty. No customers were to be seen.

"This street is dead," I remarked to Father Kent.

"The shopkeepers must be taking inventory," he answered. As he spoke, I read a poster on one of the shop doors to that effect.

Several groups of military police passed us. They asked to see our passes and we showed them the blue envelope we had received from police headquarters. As soon as they saw the blue envelope they waved us by.

Lin, the barber, who came regularly to the Mission to trim our hair, had his shop on Lion Street. When we passed by he ran out to stop Su Wen.

"Where are the priests going? Have they been expelled from Dragon Town?" he asked excitedly.

"No, they have been summoned to police headquarters," Su Wen explained.

Lin shook his head in disgust but said nothing. He re-entered his barbershop.

As we passed, other shopkeepers came to their doors. Those whom we knew bowed their heads and others stared at us. I knew that they were puzzled by our clerical clothes.

We crossed Main Street. There was more activity there. Laborers were patching the street at the crossing of Lion and Main. While they were busy pouring cement, a labor leader with a megaphone announced the news of the day in a loud, staccato voice. Work and instruction, or propaganda, were being carried on simultaneously under the People's Government. I was glad that they did not notice us. They had their backs turned, and were deeply interested in their work.

After we had passed the labor squad, we quickly reached police headquarters. I recognized the entrance at once — it formerly had been the Nationalist Army headquarters. Two stone lions mounted on limestone bases dominated the entrance. Beyond the lions was an old-fashioned arch. It looked dilapidated, for little green bushes were growing out of the yellow tiles. Beyond the ancient arch was a high brick wall with a wide entrance. At this entrance six soldiers armed with rifles and fixed bayonets were standing guard.

These guards ordered us to halt. One drew close to me and I showed him the blue envelope. It worked like magic. We were then told to proceed. Father Kent and I went on but Su Wen was stopped and refused admittance.

"Father," he called, "I can't go in. Father, you'd better take the quilts." He removed them from the ends of the carrying pole and I took one in each arm. Father Kent came back and took his quilt. The guards growled at Su Wen:

"What do you mean, serving American imperialists?"

"They are Catholic priests," Su Wen explained boldly.

"Go home," they snorted, "or we'll have you put in jail!"

We passed through the entrance. Two other guards came out of a low building adjacent to the high wall.

"Open your bundles," they commanded. We got down on our hands and knees. As I began to untie the cord around my quilt, my black hat tumbled from my head to the floor. I let it lie there beside me. I loosened my quilt, spread out the yellow canvas cloth first and then flattened out the quilt. Father Kent followed my example and when he had finished he picked up my hat and handed it to me.

The two officers then got down on their knees and carefully patted every inch of the quilts with the palms of their hands. It was only too obvious that they were searching for hidden objects. As I watched them perform their searching act I felt that it was being done to impress us. They actually would have been astonished to find a small knife or a vest-pocket revolver.

When they finished, they ordered us to roll up the quilts. I got down on my knees once again and folded the quilt in four. It was still very bulky and loose, so I tried again. I attempted to hold the folds in place with my knees. I was so awkward that the official inspectors howled and shouted:

"This foreign devil can't even fold a quilt!"

Father Kent was doing a better job, but even his bundle was much larger than the one made by Su Wen. After he had wrapped his up and tied it with the brown cord, he came over to help me but the official inspectors stopped him. They said:

"That old foreign devil must learn to do things for himself!"

I was so clumsy that I could not help laughing at my

ridiculous situation. The official inspectors were surprised that I took it with good humor. Finally I got the yellow cloth wrapped around the quilt and tied with the cord. I tugged on the cord in the hope of reducing the size of my lumpy bundle; it helped a little, but in the end it was three times its original size.

I picked it up with both hands, and tried to walk forward by holding it before me. This I managed only by resting part of it on my stomach. My arms, however, soon got tired and I swung it up on my shoulders. In so doing I again knocked off my hat. I had to lower the yellow bundle to the ground while Father Kent picked up the hat.

The two of us were now laughing like irresponsible boys. There we were, solemnly dressed in our black clerical clothes and awkwardly trying to juggle our bright yellow quilt bundles. Father Kent managed fairly well, but I felt as if I resembled a clown in the circus.

When I put my yellow bundle down, I glanced around police headquarters. It was a beehive of activity. It seemed to me that there were several hundred laborers, bricklayers, carpenters, or carriers walking around with blueprints in their hands. There might have been twenty buildings in the process of construction at one time. There, with my own eyes, I saw a tremendous building program in operation. I asked myself, are all the citizens of Dragon Town going to be put in jail?

As we walked along a narrow path, a Red soldier acted as our guide to the Foreign Affairs Department. Police personnel that happened to pass grinned when they saw us with quilts. One said:

"These foreign devils are prepared to stay here tonight.

They are soft!" He laughed at his own humor. Whoever passed our way smiled at the clumsy manner in which we carried our bundles. We were paying the penalty for my comfort-seeking.

Finally, the Red soldier guide led us to an enclosed courtyard of the spacious police headquarters grounds. In the center there was a plum tree. From one of its branches hung a bronze temple gong. We followed our guide through a small gate and as I went through it I felt as if I had entered a Communist cloister where I would probably spend the rest of my allotted span of life on earth.

Our guide said, "Wait here." I looked around. Directly opposite us there was a new, low red building, rectangular in shape. It formed one part of the enclosure. A black-and-white sign hung over its entrance: *Foreign Affairs Department.*

The other walls of the enclosure were also part of barracks-shaped buildings. A soldier came out of one and took a side glance at us. He walked up to the plum tree and struck the gong three times with a wooden mallet. Instantly a dozen doors opened and soldiers dressed in blue and khaki filed by us in silence. They all entered the Foreign Affairs Department building.

One soldier motioned to us to enter the office. We picked up our yellow bundles and walked to the entrance.

I looked into the spacious office. A beautiful Peiping rug was on the floor. I hesitated before entering. In fact, I unconsciously wiped the dust off my shoes with my trousers. I was reluctant to soil the beautiful rug with its design of a huge yellow dragon, ancient Chinese symbol of prosperity and good fortune. As I entered I was conscious that I had stepped on the dragon's tail.

The walls had been freshly whitewashed and the ceiling was painted a light blue. On the back wall hung a huge portrait of Mao Tse-Tung. The floor space was divided into sections by shiny new desks. Each desk had the name of the officer occupying it on a place card.

The office of the Foreign Affairs Department was modern, clean and orderly. There was a sofa with a small table in front of it for guests.

Father Kent and I put our quilts on the floor and sat down. We waited silently until we should be wanted. The harmonious appointments of the office certainly impressed me — no money had been spared to make it attractive. As I was admiring the setting, I heard my name called. I got up at once and went to the desk from which a soldier had beckoned to me.

"Have you your passport?"

I was flustered and began to apologize. The soldier didn't give me time to finish my sentence.

He said politely, "Bring it tomorrow at three o'clock in the afternoon. That is all."

Then he called Father Kent over. "Your passport?" he inquired.

"Sorry. I don't have it."

"Bring yours tomorrow at ten o'clock in the morning. That is all." Thus, in a moment, we were dismissed.

The soldier guide appeared again and led us to the entrance. There, the official inspectors had us untie the quilts and I went through my awkward act once again. I was tempted to leave the quilt there, I was so exhausted from handling it. In fact, I did offer it to the guards in fun but they misunderstood my meaning and were insulted.

One of them cried indignantly: "Our great leader, Mao Tse-Tung, supplies us with everything we need. We don't have to depend on America!"

Once outside we limped along with our burdens. Who should come out of a small restaurant but Su Wen! He was surprised to see us so soon. He had stopped at Lan's Restaurant for a dish of noodles. I was very happy to see him and, as he shouldered the quilts, we followed him in perfect peace.

"How about tomorrow's session, John?" Father Kent asked. "Taking your quilt along?"

"No. I'd rather die from the cold than go through all that embarrassment again!" I answered firmly.

"What do you think of their plan to have us appear separately?" Father Kent asked.

"We are pawns in their hands, Frank," I replied. "They possess the cunning of Lucifer. Only St. Michael the Archangel can save us." I was despondent and knew that the Bird of Sorrow was once again hovering over my head. The Bird of Sorrow disappeared, however, when I saw Madame Wu's wrinkled face light up with happiness as she beheld us coming down the street.

"No need for chicken soup tomorrow," I called. "Perhaps the following day."

Father Kent and I walked on as Su Wen related to Madame Wu that we were required to appear at police headquarters once again the next day.

Little did we know.

This was only the beginning. For fifteen consecutive days we were told to report to police headquarters. Each time we thought it was our last journey!

13

Ma Chung Wins a Battle

It WAS DARK when **Ma** Chung came to my room. Spread out before me on the desk were Mission property deeds. They were written on a fine rice paper that had turned yellow with age. The deeds dated back to 1900. I had taken them out of the Mission safe because Secretary Ma Chung had to present them to the land office for registration under the People's Government.

"Glad to see you," I said as he entered. "We need to make a record of the deeds before you take them to the land office."

"It is a waste of time, Father," Ma Chung said gruffly.

I was startled by his abrupt tone. Never before had I heard Ma Chung give vent to his feelings. His usual calm bearing had disappeared and discontent marked his countenance.

"What do you mean?" I asked gently.

"You will be expelled from China in a short time," he replied, endeavoring to conceal his ill-humor.

"That is no surprise," I responded sadly. "We live in a topsy-turvy world."

"Father, it is more than that," he burst out. "It is a cruel world, and I can't bear it any longer. I have decided to surrender. I will go tonight and give myself up to Captain Fu."

I knew that we had been living on top of a volcano. However, I had not expected the eruption to come from Ma Chung.

"I can understand your feelings, Ma Chung," I said, "and I must make a confession to you. Whenever I have been tempted to capitulate myself, I have thought of you, and I have been inspired by your splendid example of courage and fortitude. But," I appealed to him, "you can't give up now, Ma Chung. To surrender is to despair. Despair is in Hell."

"You speak noble language, Father," he answered shortly. "But permit me to pour out my heart without reserve or respect for my elders. Let me begin with you, Father. Have you seen the *Red Star Daily?*" he asked sharply.

"No," I replied, as I wondered what had brought on Ma Chung's belligerent attitude. That morning, I recalled, when we had made out the Mission financial report, Ma Chung was cheerful.

"Li Li Pan has made the headlines again," he said bitterly. "It is terrible news. I don't have the heart to repeat it. I have lost hope in human nature." His face was dark with despair.

Without another word I jumped from my seat and rushed to the library to get the *Red Star* newspaper. I unfolded it, and was stricken with horror as I read the headline:

LI LI PAN VOLUNTEERS TO STAB HER GRANDFATHER, PAN TAO, TO DEATH FOR HIS CRIMES AGAINST THE PEOPLE'S GOVERNMENT.

Shaken and alarmed, I returned to my room. Ma Chung sat crushed, his face covered with his hands. I wished to sympathize, to place my hands on his shoulders. But I did not dare to approach him. What could I say? What could I do? He loved Li Li Pan. What a staggering blow to him!

In desperation, I drew my rosary beads out of my pocket and paced the floor of my room, earnestly supplicating Heaven for aid in this dark hour.

After a while Ma Chung looked up at me. In a subdued voice he said: "I went over to see Li Li Pan. I asked her, 'Is it true, Li Li?'

"She was very casual: 'What are you talking about, Ma Chung?'

" 'The news in the *Red Star*, Li Li.'

" 'What news, Ma Chung?'

" 'About your honorable grandfather.' I held out the newspaper to her.

" 'Every word in the *Red Star* is true,' affirmed Li Li.

" 'Then you mean, Li Li, that you will be present at your grandfather's trial?' I asked.

" 'Of course. I was the first to denounce him.'

" 'Will he be condemned to death?'

" 'Certainly. His crimes cry to Heaven for justice.'

" 'Will you,' I faltered, 'stab him to death?'

" 'Of course. I have agreed,' Li Li Pan interjected.

" 'No! No!' I shouted as I suddenly clasped Li Li Pan in my arms. 'You are too beautiful. You must not stain your innocent hands with human blood! I love you! I must protect you! We will run away together!' I cried like a wild man.

"We were standing outside the front door of her house. Li Li Pan forced herself free from my embrace. She slapped me across the face and, grasping my arm, pulled me inside the house. The blow on the cheek broke my emotional tension.

"Li Li Pan then led me to the reception room and pushed me into a chair. She served me a cup of tea. Sipping the hot tea, I recovered my self-control.

" 'Look at me, Li Li. Are you not out of your mind?'

" 'No!' Li Li answered emphatically. 'People like my grandfather, Pan Tao, must die!'

" 'You are possessed by the devil, Li Li!'

" 'Control your tongue, Ma Chung.'

" 'I would rather die with your grandfather, Li Li, than serve the devil.'

" 'Who is the devil, Ma Chung?'

" 'Mao Tse-Tung, the leader, in whose name you are willing to sin against filial piety,' I replied. 'The master Confucius said: "Filial piety is the law of Heaven, the principle of earth, and the path of men." '

"Li Li Pan responded scornfully, 'Our country has followed the Confucian teaching for three thousand years. With what results? We are the most despised nation in the world and the poorest people on earth!' She continued: 'Listen, Ma Chung, give up your old ideas. Filial piety must go.'

" 'Love can never die, Li Li. It is eternal.'

" 'Certainly. Love of country, Ma Chung.'

" 'No. Love of parents,' I remonstrated. 'That comes first. It is as natural as water flowing downhill. Li Li, if your honorable grandfather must die for treason, why does not the law treat him as other criminals?'

" 'I must do as I am told,' Li Li Pan responded. 'That is the first great law of the People's Government.'

" 'Why cannot your honorable grandfather face the firing squad? The truth is, Li Li, you are not trusted by the Communist officials. This is to test your loyalty to the Red Party.'

" 'Nevertheless, I do it gladly.'

" 'But it is unjust, Li Li!'

" 'Nothing is unjust for the advancement of Communism.'

"Father, our conversation was like a duel — steel against steel. I had taken the initiative. I wished with all my soul to dissuade her from the heinous crime. I realized that arguments from reason were useless. I tried a new approach — appeal to the heart. Many times on the university campus we had related stories in reference to members of our respective families. On the table in the reception room there was a Parker 51. I picked it up and revolved it in my fingers. I looked up at Li Li Pan and asked:

" 'Who gave you this pen?'

"Li Li Pan snatched it out of my hands without saying a word. Next I took up from the table a gold wrist watch — a Gruen — as attractive as Li Li Pan herself. I held it long enough in my hand to read aloud the inscription: *Li Li Pan, 18th Birthday, from Grandpa Pan Tao, 1950.* Li Li Pan seized it out of my hand and clasped it on her wrist.

" 'Who is Pan Tao's favorite granddaughter? Who taught Li Li to talk and walk? Who showed Li Li how to hold the pen brush? Who read the classics to Li Li, and wrote poetry in her honor? Of course, her affectionate grandfather! Who drilled Li Li in the ancient songs of China? Patient Pan Tao. Who named the birds and flowers for Li Li? Devoted grandfather, Pan Tao!'

" 'Stop!' Li Li Pan shrieked. 'Go!' Li Li Pan said, as she pointed impetuously to the door. 'You are breaking my heart,' she cried. 'Grandfather must die! China must live!' she added emphatically. 'Go! Go! Go!'

"I departed. Fortunately, Li Li Pan was in the house alone. Her parental home is now occupied by the university girl students. They are the hard core of the girls' youth movement. Li Li Pan is the shining star of the unit. Her comrades were out at the time, checking registration cards on the front doors of the houses on Main Street."

When Young Ma had finished his dramatic account of his meeting with Li Li Pan, I got out of my chair and went over to him. Ma Chung was shaking. I offered him a cigarette, and got him a cup of tea. After drinking it, he began to talk again. Relieving his pent-up feelings was like ridding himself of poison.

"That is not all, Father. After I left Li Li Pan, I tasted more bitterness. I ran into Li Li Pan's parents on Lion Street. I was horrified by their deplorable condition. They were dressed in rags; their pinched faces showed signs of hunger. They looked haggard from lack of sleep. Madame Pan was leaning on her husband's arm. Mr. Pan had an empty rice bowl in his hand. He recognized me and in a hollow voice whispered my name. I bent forward and grasped their arms, wishing to rescue them from their misery. It was dark, and I led them to the nearest doorway. I made them sit down, thinking that I could comfort them. I looked at the empty rice bowl, and instinctively asked them whether they had eaten.

"Mr. Pan answered that no one had given them any food all day. This was the first time that someone they had approached had not slammed the door in their faces. He was puzzled. He did not know the cause. I could easily have explained about their daughter, Li Li Pan, but I left them in ignorance.

" 'Wait here,' I told them, as I hurried to a bakery shop nearby and bought some bread, which has become common now in Dragon Town because the soldiers of the Red Army are from North China. I also borrowed a pot of tea from the shopkeeper, and brought the food and drink to them. I sat with them while they ate the bread and drank the tea.

"Fortunately it was a dark night — there were no stars or moon in the sky. Mr. Pan told me they had just been released from jail. Their punishment was that they had to beg from door to door and sleep in the temples on the outskirts of town. I would have spent the whole night with them, but Mr. Pan told me to leave them, otherwise I would get in trouble. They were especially afraid that the police might find me with them, and then I would be arrested.

"He told me that when some old friend was particularly nice to them, for two or three days they were shadowed by a detective. On those days they went absolutely hungry, for no one dared to offer them food.

"How can I go on living, Father? I would rather hang! At least it would be a protest against the abominations of the Communist order.

"Moreover, now I lead a lonely life. On the street, my friends pass me by like a stranger; some even cross to the other side of the street if they see me coming in their direction; others turn back from whence they have come purposely to avoid me. They shun me like a leper. Even your merchant friends, Father, have served me notice to keep out of their shops.

"My friends march and sing, full of new hope for China as they follow the Red flag — while I stand by and lament over the old world which has passed away."

I was sick at heart, listening to Ma Chung pour out his bitter tale. "I can sympathize with you," I said to him. "You know how well I was acquainted in Dragon Town. Now I am the despised foreigner. I feel for you, Ma Chung. You are young, life is dear to you — yet you must hope. That light must shine in you like a dot in a vast dark world."

"How can I hope, Father?" he asked. "Communism is like the boa constrictor that attains great length and crushes its prey in its coils. It has already begun to bind me. Strangulation will be my end.

"When I am not roaming the street alone I have no privacy. My room is like a public place. Soldiers come to visit me, one after the other, any time of the day or night. No matter how the conversation begins, it always ends on the same note. Soldiers say to me I must keep in mind that I am a Chinese, that I must be patriotic, and that I should denounce the foreigners as spies.

"Captain Fu haunts me. He calls on me every day. He urges me to tell him where the foreigners have installed the broadcasting set with which they communicate with America. Captain Fu tells me he knows that you have the set, and he is almost certain that I know where it is hidden in the house, but I won't inform him.

"He said to me: 'You have reverence for foreigners and you think that they love you. You are deceived. Let me tell

you that when the foreigners are expelled from our country and they return to America, they will reside in beautiful homes and live like kings, eat three meals a day, wear
fine clothes and ride in luxurious automobiles — they will
forget all about you. After the foreigners have been expelled, what will become of you? No one will hire you;
no one will dare to give you a room in his house. You will
have to sleep in the temples at night. You will not be able
to eat from the people's rice basket, and therefore you will
have to beg for your food. Have you thought of it — that
you will slowly starve to death? After you are dead the foreigners will not be here to weep over you or accompany
you to the grave. Is there anything more pitiable in life
than a corpse without a mourner?'

"Captain Fu's words kept pouring into my ears like
water. I felt as if I were drowning. In the beginning, in
my innocence, I argued with him. Later I let him go on
like a victrola, without interrupting.

"Once, when Captain Sun came along with Captain Fu
to see me, they gave me the water treatment. It was a
special evening for them. I had been sarcastic and they
decided to tame me. I had to sit down in my chair while
Captain Sun, with a water pitcher in his hand, stood over
me. Slowly he let fall on my neck drop after drop of water.

"At first I merely felt a cool sensation. Next, I began to
shiver; and as the drip, drip of the water drops fell on my
neck, I shook like a leaf. A little later my nerves began to
tingle, and as the strain of my nervous tension increased,
I shrieked and jumped out of my chair. I ran around the
room like a madman, then turned on Captain Sun. I
tried to clutch his throat, but Captain Fu stepped in to
prevent me.

"Captain Fu daily goads me, especially about you. He says that I should distrust you, Father. I should insinuate that you are a spy; I should pretend that I inform on you; I should keep you in suspense; I should neglect my duties to provoke you; I should incessantly demand a higher salary to embarrass you; I should mentally torture you with innumerable annoyances.

"It is a steady grind to wear me down. He hopes to get me to dislike you, and then to hate you. It is a daily pressure. I cannot sleep at night. I feel the invisible hand of Captain Fu slowly choking me. It is Hell to live, Father. I would rather die. Yes, hang."

I groaned at the realization of the sufferings of our faithful friend.

"Captain Fu is trying to brain-wash you, Ma Chung," I said. "He is attempting to sow the seed of discontent in your soul; terrorizing you so that you will ruin the Mission. How nobly you have stood up to him so far! Pray and keep telling him the truth! At least you will have peace of soul. Trust in God, my son."

Ma Chung was silent for a moment, then began again, trying to be polite but with resentment showing through. "Please excuse me, Father," he said, glancing at me. "You, too, agreed with those who said the Reds would never conquer China. 'The Chinese are too individualistic,' you all said; 'they will not yield to regimentation.' How often have I heard it said: 'Everything will be all right. It can't happen here!'

"Why have the Red demons taken over China? Because too many old people have been too complacent. They talk wisely, but do nothing practical. The house is on fire, and still they appease the world and the young with oratory. Who suffers from the stupidity of the old? The young, like myself. We are caught in the Red net, because the old have failed in their duty to keep the world free. The Reds have been increasing for years, they rule half the world, and yet old people like you still only talk in eloquent language."

He paused for breath, then went on:

"I am sorry to talk to you in this bold manner, like one who has no filial piety. But it is true, Father. You know it, and the whole world knows it, too."

I was shaken. There was an element of truth in all that this sorely-tried young man was saying. His mental torment became my own. Would the blunders of my generation cause him to turn against all the truths we believed in? My concern for his soul grew — surrender would mean despair! How could I check it? Prayer and his own goodness — not any words of mine — would have to decide the answer.

"Follow your conscience, Ma Chung," I said with resignation.

"My conscience, Father, is cruel," he said desperately. "It reprimands, scolds, but it does not comfort me. It says I am a coward and I should be strong, a man with faith and hope. It haunts me worse than Captain Fu. I go mad, Father, until I fall on my knees and pray."

Near midnight Father Kent came to my room. He brought us tea whereupon Ma Chung repeated all he had to say to Father Kent. This emptying of his soul was a purgation. It went on until dawn. Three times Ma Chung wept like a child. He wished to do the right thing, fight on, but the temptation to surrender kept recurring.

After dawn broke we all went to the church together. We knelt until it was time for the daily Mass at seven o'clock. Ma Chung served my Mass. I offered it up for him with the prayer: "Through grace, God, give him peace of soul."

14

The Captains Demand an Inventory

At breakfast I was silent and exhausted. Su Wen served me two fried eggs and a piece of bread, and poured my coffee. I saluted Father Kent with a nod of my head when he came to the table.

I was relieved that Ma Chung had not capitulated, and so felt a certain sense of victory. Nevertheless, my spirits were low.

I rose from the table, and went straight to my room and shut the door. The morning sun was shining through the east window. I drew the blue curtain to keep out the sun. Darkness suited my melancholy mood. I slipped off my cloth shoes and threw myself on the bed, spreading a gray blanket over me.

With my head on the pillow, I felt my body relax. As my tired nerves quieted down, my mind roamed far off to New Rochelle where I was born. I saw myself as a boy,

strolling down a shady lane as happy as a lark. I entered a
green-shingled house, and as I ran up the stairs, I realized I
was home and I began shouting: "Ma!" as I did every
day when I returned from school. This scene suddenly
vanished, to my disappointment. I dropped off to sleep.

But now I dreamed that hard-looking Captain Sun had
entered my room and was standing at my bedside. He
glared at me with his cold, beady eyes. I could tell by the
ugly expression on his face that he had come to murder
me. I attempted to get out of bed, but discovered that I
was tied with ropes. I struggled to get loose. I was helpless.
Instead of allowing fear to grip me, I defiantly shouted at
him: "Shoot, you Communist devil!" His cold pin-point
eyes pierced me, but I stared boldly back at him. He
curled his thin lips and reached for his gun.

Suddenly I heard a crash at my window like a violent
gust of wind. I saw thousands of vultures rush into the
room. They alighted and clung fast to the captain and in
a moment they covered him from head to foot so that all
I could see of him were those terrifying eyes — cruel, cold,
black dots. The vultures lifted him bodily and carried
him away through the window like a corpse. The tumult
of the vultures faded off in the distance, but I was being
shaken from head to foot.

I heard Kent's voice say, "Get up, John." What was he
doing with the vultures? I opened my eyes, and saw
Father Kent standing anxiously over me.

"Hurry, John," he said. "The captains are waiting for
you in the parlor."

"Captains? Not Captain Sun?" I groaned, without rais-
ing my head from the pillow.

"Yes, Sun and Fu. Both captains are here," Father Kent
replied.

"It can't be, Frank. I just saw a legion of vultures bearing Sun away."

"You've been dreaming, John."

Now, at last, I was fully awake. My forehead was wet with perspiration. I moved my right hand. It was free. I was ridiculously relieved, and I raised it to wipe my brow. "I'm alive, Frank," I said, as I jumped out of bed. I slipped into my cloth shoes, and repeated gratefully, "I am not dead yet. It's wonderful!"

"Hurry, John," Father Kent said again. "The captains seem to be pressed for time."

"You go ahead, Frank. I'll follow you in a moment."

I washed my face, flattened my hair, slipped into my cassock and snatched my hat and overcoat. I joined the captains and Father Kent in the parlor.

As I entered the parlor there was no doubt about it — the two captains were there. They were wearing parade uniforms: brown jackets and gray trousers. I glanced first at gaunt Captain Sun. His cold eyes met mine. I dropped my eyes immediately, as I could not bear the evil stare. Around his narrow waist he wore a leather belt, but today there was no gun dangling at his side. On his shoulder there were the bars of his rank. Dangling from his chest I saw two silver stars. Above them were pinned five combat ribbons. Beside him, Captain Fu, who always acted as the spokesman, displayed no medals but he also had five combat ribbons pinned to his uniform.

Without any introduction Captain Fu said: "Here are some forms for an inventory of the things in the Mission house." He passed them to me, and added, "Have these forms ready in two days."

I accepted the papers and the two captains walked quickly out of the room. I should have liked to tell them

about the vultures, just to see their reaction. As Father
Kent and I turned our attention to the inventory forms,
Ma Chung entered the parlor. He looked rested. Like myself, he had taken a nap. He showed signs of embarrassment, because of his outburst of the previous night. I endeavored to put him at ease by telling him:

"We have to make an inventory of our possessions. I
want to ask you to help us fill out the forms." I passed the
forms to him and he looked through them, then asked:
"When do we begin?"

"Let us start now," I replied.

"Father," Ma Chung noted, "besides recording each
article, we must paste labels on them, stating number and
price value."

Ma Chung sat at the table in the middle of the parlor.
He started the inventory with articles of furniture. There
were three bamboo chairs and three straight-back chairs
in the parlor. We registered these first. Father Kent and
I pasted on the labels. While we were engaged in this
operation for the People's Government two awkward-
looking soldiers sheepishly entered the parlor. They bent
over the table to see what Ma Chung was writing. He
inquired of them what business they had, and they made
no reply. They simply gaped at him with mouths wide
open.

After I had pasted a label on one of the chairs, the two
soldiers together raised it aloft, and holding it above their
heads, they inspected the bottom of it. They followed this
procedure with other chairs, giving the appearance of
amateur acrobats. They looked stupid, but seemed to be
enjoying their own performance.

I pasted a label on the small tea table in the corner of

the room. They crouched under it, and banged the bottom with their fists. The teacups on the table danced, and one tumbled to the floor. It broke into two pieces and each soldier picked up a half. Ashamed at what they had done, they placed the pieces on the tea table and silently departed.

Their behavior was so unlike the disciplined soldiers of the Red Army that I was at a loss to comprehend its significance. Actually, Father Kent, Ma Chung and I were amused at their queer actions and had a hearty laugh. This was a real treat for us, because laughter was not a daily tonic behind the bamboo curtain.

As I pasted a label on my portable victrola on the table opposite, another pair of soldiers — rough and stout — entered. One had a knife cut on the right cheek and the other had large black eyes, like a Westerner, a long nose, and a dark beard. They looked like bandits, instead of members of the regular Red Army. Their uniforms were light blue, and they carried sidearms. For a moment I thought I was beholding two buccaneers, Chinese-style, from a pirate ship. I was on my knees and jumped up quickly. Father Kent was moving books from the bookcase. He stood still, holding several volumes in his hands. Ma Chung stopped writing and fixed his gaze on these two powerful and dominating new arrivals.

They lifted the victrola from its stand and brought it over to Ma Chung's table. Towering over him, the soldier with the large black eyes demanded: "What is this?"

Ma Chung told him it was a music box. The soldier with the cut on his cheek countered: "We don't believe it."

Hearing him say so, I picked a humorous Chinese record out of the pile on the bookcase. Its slapstick title was:

"The Old Woman Innkeeper whose husband had a face as round as the moon and a belly as large as a grave mound and drank wine like rice gruel out of a soup bowl." I played it for them, and they bent over with laughter.

When it was finished, the rough, simple souls said to Ma Chung: "We were told that the machine was a broadcasting set. Tell the foreign devils they have a sense of humor."

After they had gone Ma Chung told us that this type of Red Army soldier formerly lived as bandits in the mountains, and were now used as mountain scouts.

We had just begun to record and label the books in the bookcase when still another pair of soldiers came in to see what we were doing. These two soldiers were slight in stature; they were southern Chinese, with very fine features. They were dressed in the green uniforms of the Red Army. In their vest pockets they carried fountain pens. Both of them wore wrist watches. They wore no insignia of rank and looked like young college men.

Father Kent kept removing the volumes from the shelves. Ma Chung recorded the titles and translated them into Chinese while I pasted the labels on the backs of the books. It was a mixed collection — history, theology, novels, poetry, etc. There was a thick volume, *The Last Stand,* a history of the Communist threat written by Father Walsh, S. J., many years ago.

The soldiers said nothing. They moved around the room, observing us at work. They looked at the victrola, opened the record album, inspected a statue of the Blessed Mother in the bookcase. It had been carved by a Chinese artist, and the features of the Blessed Mother were Chinese. They discussed the statue between themselves, and I overheard one say: "It must be the Goddess of Mercy."

Then one soldier picked up *The Last Stand*. He opened it and, pointing to a page, called it to the attention of his comrade. I heard the first soldier say, "This is a book on Communism." He passed it to the second soldier, who sat down and began to read it. Then I saw him take a pad out of his pocket and begin to make notes. I wished to say something to Father Kent, but I did not dare do so. Certainly the second soldier understood. He read attentively and copied passages from the book.

I blamed myself for not having destroyed that book and several others. The thought had come to me in the past, but I had not carried it out. No doubt he would report to Captain Fu and some of the quotations would appear in the *Red Star Daily*. We had destroyed the Chinese books, or cut out the pages about Communism, but here was a whole book in English. I felt my stomach churning.

I could not bear to watch the soldier read *The Last Stand*. I left the parlor and went to my own room. The idea came to me that perhaps Ma Chung had been truly right last night. It was useless to try to hold out against the Reds. Give up. Go to jail. Hang. Be shot. All these were better than to be hunted and haunted as we were, according to some sort of fixed plan.

As I turned over these despairing thoughts I lit a cigarette and stood looking out my window at a fisherman wading along the bank, setting egg-shaped bamboo traps for a night catch of fish. Did such peacefulness exist? I turned my head toward the open door of my room. It hardly came as a surprise to see two more corpulent soldiers, who looked like bakers, standing in the doorway watching me. My dream of the vultures was turning into reality. I felt that by evening I would be the victim of the Red vultures. Perhaps I, too, would be carried away like a corpse.

I invited them to come into my room, and they accepted my invitation. With their hands behind their backs, they gazed around at every item, like connoisseurs of antiques.

The portable typewriter on my desk attracted their attention. One soldier with his pudgy index finger punched a key heavily, and it struck the letter K on the white sheet of paper in the machine. He pressed several keys which printed on the white sheet of paper. The other soldier picked up the machine and examined the bottom of it. He shook it; the carriage sprang and the bell rang. They jumped back in alarm. When nothing more deadly followed, I heard this conversation between them:

First Soldier: "It prints foreign letters."

Second Soldier: "It is a foreign machine."

First Soldier: "Those letters are a code for sending messages to America."

Second Soldier: "The tap, tap sound is transmitted through the air to America."

I was not able to keep silent any longer. Boldly I took the typewriter out of their hands. They were surprised at my action. I pushed them aside, and placed the typewriter on the desk again. I rapidly wrote sentences. I whipped the white paper out of the machine and told them: "Take this to someone who understands English. Ask them what it means. They will tell you it comes from a writing machine."

The two soldiers answered, "That is right. It constructs messages for America about our great country, China."

I firmly answered, "No!"

They retorted smugly, "American foreigners clever people. You an American, clever, too."

A harsh voice from outside my window called them. I did not look out the window, but the corpulent visitors departed immediately, leaving me fuming at their stupidity. Had I a club in my hand, I thought, how I would be tempted to use it on their thick heads!

At the same time I had an instinct that this was exactly what the subtle Captain Fu hoped I would do! What a headline it would make: "Imperialist Spy Attacks People's Representatives!"

I was so discouraged that I felt as if a hundred birds of sorrow were nestled in my hair. I decided to go to the church to pray before more soldiers should come to aggravate me. But I was not to escape so easily!

I had only stepped out into the corridor when I saw two tall, slim soldiers standing outside Father Kent's room.

I heard Father Kent's voice in the parlor, patiently explaining the victrola to several soldiers. I was curious as to what the two soldiers were doing in front of Father Kent's room. They might be planning to frame Father Kent by hiding a revolver in his room. I had no proof for this, except that I had known it done to others. I was suspicious but curbed myself and did not disturb them.

I passed the dining room. The two pudgy soldiers stood looking at Su Wen setting the supper table. I heard one remark: "The knives, forks and spoons are made of silver." Another said: "These are expensive; the foreigners are rich." For a moment I wondered whether I should try to explain the capitalist mystery of cheap silver-plated knives and forks. Then I realized they would never believe me anyhow!

I passed on, feeling sorry for poor Su Wen. He, like Ma Chung, was constantly under pressure. Soldiers were in and out of his kitchen daily, either to plague him with questions, or to borrow kitchen utensils. Sometimes, as he was preparing our supper, soldiers would come to order him at once to attend a people's meeting. When that happened, Su Mei took over and Su Li served the food. Sometimes Father Kent and I prepared our own meals while the Su family were out on duty for the People's Government.

Su Wen told me that oftentimes they were ordered away, hoping that I would get angry. Especially when Su Wen would be allowed to return right *after* we had cooked the meal, served it for ourselves and washed the dishes. Su Wen was always apologizing about it, God bless his soul. The more annoying the Reds were, the more faithful he was to us.

I walked across the courtyard and saw Su Li feeding the American chicken, with a dozen soldiers at his side. Really, here in Dragon Town, the turkey had become a far better known symbol of the United States than the bald eagle ever was.

I passed the open door of Ma Chung's room. Four soldiers looked as if they were holding a conversation with him. I heard a harsh voice say, "The Americans have a plot to conquer China."

I had every confidence in Ma Chung, but the oppression was getting beyond human bearing.

In front of the Su house two buxom women soldiers were standing around Su Mei as she ironed the Mission linen. The women soldiers talked rapidly. As I passed I heard them say: "Women must be interested in politics and help make China strong."

Su Mei, a small, gentle woman, without answering steadily moved her charcoal iron back and forth with a dull look in her eyes.

This afternoon a special effort was being made by the Reds to stir up trouble in the Mission compound. We had lived like goldfish in a bowl since "liberation," but this was the first organized movement to frighten all the Mission workers at the same time. I certainly needed to pray that they would stand up under the concentrated strain!

I went across to the church and opened my Breviary. I was kneeling in the last pew when I heard the church door open. I did not stir. Next, I felt a hand tap me on the shoulder. I looked up and it was one of the women soldiers who had been talking to Su Mei. I got up and walked back to the vestibule of the church.

"Father," she asked in a high-pitched voice, "please let us borrow the vestments you wear in the performance of your Catholic rituals."

"I am sorry," I answered politely, "but that is impossible."

"Why, Father?" the other asked. "We intend to use them in a play."

"The vestments are sacred. Only a priest is permitted to wear them in a ceremony."

"We were sent here to obtain the vestments; they are needed for the first act and we must have them."

"I am sorry, but you ask for something I cannot give you," I declared as I re-entered the church.

I was disturbed, and instead of kneeling to read my Breviary, I paced back and forth, up and down the aisle.

The two women now entered the church together and sat in the last pew, whispering to each other. I had no idea what they were talking about. Then they rose from the pew by the side aisle and walked up to the sanctuary. They paused before the altar and opened the side gate of the sanctuary railing and crossed to the sacristy, where there was a vestment case containing ceremonial robes used in celebrating the Mass and other services.

I closed my Breviary and followed them into the sacristy. One soldier had already pulled open the closet containing the red vestments. I quickly stepped up to her side and pushed it closed. I almost caught her fingers in the door.

"You stupid and stingy foreigner!" the woman soldier yelled at me.

I said nothing, but placed my back against the vestment case.

"We must have the red vestments," the second soldier shouted. "Step aside, Father!"

I did not move. The first soldier reached for her small revolver. I still held my ground. She leveled it at my head. I looked her straight in the eye. If I were going to die, I might as well die saving the church vestments.

"The foreigner is stubborn," the second soldier remarked. "The foreigner is brave," the first replied as she put up her gun. "That is why he is in China as a spy."

I answered back: "I am no spy. I am a Catholic priest. These vestments are used to worship the True God. It is unreasonable to use them in a play."

Footsteps sounded in the church. I was fortunate. They were the footsteps of Su Wen. He entered the sacristy and was taken by surprise to see me standing with my back against the vestment case. Looking at me, Su Wen announced calmly, "Father, your supper is on the table." To the women soldiers he said: "You know the Father must eat."

It was strange. At the word "eat," the two women soldiers became reasonable human beings. Glaring at me in a disappointed manner, they walked out of the sacristy mumbling.

I knelt down at the altar rail and said a prayer in thanksgiving for still being alive. Su Wen and I went out together. Su Wen locked the church. He did so of his own accord. He was afraid the women might come back and take the vestments. I had the feeling they would not come back, but I did not say anything to him.

I returned to the rectory and entered the parlor to find it was empty. I was elated. Perhaps the rectory had ceased for the evening to be a foreign showplace for the Red Army.

What a vain hope! As I stepped into the dining room I saw ten soldiers lined up along both sides of the room.

They turned their cold eyes on me. Ironically, I said to Father Kent: "There are only two places at the table, and we have ten guests."

"They are observers, John," he said in a reproving way. "They already have had their supper."

I looked up and saw the soldier guests with pencils and pads. Each was occupied in making notes on our performance at the dinner table. Normally I would have been embarrassed, but I was becoming accustomed to being in a fishbowl and having people stare at me. The Reds were indeed closing in on us!

Su Wen entered the dining room carrying a tray. Our

main meal was in the evening. Twice a week we had meat. Tonight he served us an egg soup with bits of pork, small thin steaks with onions, string beans and a large bowl of rice. We also had coffee and a piece of plain cake. The supper was good, and I was hungry. For a little while I forgot the soldier guests looking on as we manipulated our "silver" knives and forks. When we had finished the dinner, we walked out of the room, leaving the soldiers behind in the dining room.

As Su Wen came to clear off the table I could still hear their questions: "Why do you work for the foreigners?" "Why don't you leave them tonight?" "Are they not American spies?"

I was sick at heart. I was tempted to go out and give them a piece of my mind, but it was no use. I shut my door; I didn't want to hear any more.

15

I Bandy Words with Captain Fu

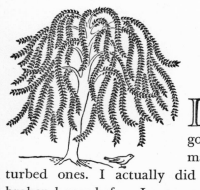

I THOUGHT I might get a good long night's sleep to make up for the past disturbed ones. I actually did get three delightful unbroken hours before I was roused to see two familiar unpleasant figures standing in the doorway — Captain Sun, the Scarecrow, and Captain Fu, the Gallant Knight! Needless to say, my spirits dropped.

"Father," Captain Fu said in his melodious voice, "we are sorry to disturb you after dark."

I looked at my watch. It was eleven o'clock.

"What is it that you want of me, Captain Fu?"

"Ten soldiers are in your courtyard, Father," Captain Fu answered. "They are in need of quarters." He asked appealingly, "Will you be so kind as to yield your parlor to my comrades?"

Since I was accustomed to his polite manner, I was not touched by his suave, hypocritical voice.

I adopted his own mode of speech. I said politely, as I clasped my chin with my right hand and pretended I was in deep thought: "I will have to study your question. Please come back tomorrow."

This was the standard Party-line reply to questions which would receive "No" for an answer.

Captain Sun scowled, and shifted his beady eyes toward me. I felt as if he were going to stretch out his bony hand and wring my neck for my sarcastic remark. I saw him writhe as he moved his hand in the direction of his revolver. Captain Fu showed no signs of irritation. He was too clever to manifest his displeasure.

"But Father," he pleaded, "the soldiers are here; they are tired and hungry. I have already told them that you are kind, and generous, and always ready to help people. Don't disappoint them, Father." His ingenuousness stiffened my resistance.

"Why do you come to ask me?" I queried, knowing how often he did as he pleased.

"Soldiers of the Red Army," Captain Fu asserted proudly, "would never occupy your parlor without your consent." He was too adept at double talk, and I resented it.

"If you need my permission," I responded, "give me this evening to think it over, and I ask you kindly to come back in the morning for an answer." I was determined to play their own game of postponement. "Moreover," I added boldly, "if you really require my approval, I don't wish to grant it to you. Where would I receive you when you came to see me? Are you not here several times a day?"

I was indiscreet to have spoken like that, but the words

came out of my mouth before I realized what I was saying. It was a case of "from the abundance of the heart, the mouth speaketh."

"Just as you say, Father," Captain Fu said calmly. "I had thought that you would consider it a great honor to receive the brave soldiers of the Red Army into your house."

Captain Sun endeavored to wither me by flashing his cruel slit eyes. I had turned down the Red Army and for a change I had a feeling of triumph.

The captains turned on their heels and went outside. In the courtyard the electric lights were on. From the parlor door I could see the ten soldiers sitting on their blanket rolls. They scrambled to their feet as the two captains approached them. Captain Fu went into Ma Chung's room. In a moment Captain Fu reappeared with Ma Chung following him, his quilt in his arms. Ma Chung came straight to the parlor door.

"Father," he said, as he saw me standing in the doorway, "Captain Fu requested me to permit the soldiers to have my room. He sent me to you. May I sleep in the rectory tonight?"

"Come in, Ma Chung," I said. "I am glad to have you. I am sorry you are inconvenienced in this manner."

"Father, I feel safer with you," he declared. "I don't sleep well in my room. I am restless lying in bed, obsessed by the fear that Captain Sun may come to take me away. The other day Su Wen told me that at the People's meeting on Tiger Street there was a rumor that some night soon Captain Sun is coming for both of us. He is certain that you are a spy, and that I am your aide."

"Ma Chung," I said, looking at him, "truly then all our uncertainties will be over."

"I suppose so," Ma Chung said bravely. "But Father, life is precious."

"You're right, Ma Chung. Could you make a break for the hills tonight? What have you got to lose? I will help you get out by the back gate. You can go upstream, and by dawn reach the foothills."

"It is no use, Father. I was warned by Captain Fu not to run away. Besides, Father, I don't think anything will happen until after Li Li Pan's grandfather, Pan Tao, has been executed. It is all part of a far-reaching plan of the Reds. After Pan Tao's death Captain Fu expects Li Li Pan to turn on me, and perhaps even you, Father."

"Therefore, Ma Chung, now is the time for you to escape."

"Father! Don't you understand?" Ma Chung said softly. "There is Li Li."

"The good Lord help us," I sighed.

It was true — we were all doomed — yet we had to live in hope.

Ma Chung left his quilt on a chair in the parlor and together we went to the library to see Father Kent. He was there working leisurely on the inventory, as though he were doing a crossword puzzle. Unlike me, he was not worried about the shadows of impending doom.

Ma Chung, who was always happy at work, began to help Father Kent. My mind could not free itself from the thought of beautiful Li Li Pan and Ma Chung. No wonder a legion of birds of sorrow hovered over me, and I went mournfully to my room. I was dead tired. After tossing from side to side for a while, I fell asleep in my chair, moving my lips in prayer for Li Li Pan and Ma Chung.

16
A Spy Hunt Nabs Felix the Cat

It was two nights later. I awoke with a start, sat up in bed and switched on the light in my room. I looked at the alarm clock on my desk. It was one o'clock. Military footsteps sounded out in the corridor. I heard Father Kent's voice. He said quietly: "Ma Chung, if Captain Fu has ordered a house inspection, we can't stop him."

At the word "inspection," I jumped out of bed and quickly dressed myself. Despite the fact that I had heard there was going to be a search of the rectory, I again had the premonition that Captain Fu really intended to march me off to jail. I took down my overcoat and hat from the hook behind the door. I even stuck a change of underwear, shirt and socks, and a face towel in the deep pockets of my overcoat. The pockets bulged hugely, but I did not realize it. My mind was entirely occupied with the thought that *this* was the night.

I went out into the corridor, and found Father Kent waiting. He eyed the clothes bursting out of my overcoat pockets.

"This is only a house inspection," he said, with a grin. "When Captain Fu sees the shirt and socks dangling out of your pockets, he may feel he has to live up to your expectations by taking you to jail."

"Well, Frank," I replied, "there's nothing like being prepared. I've heard that in Communist jails the People's Government does not provide striped uniforms."

I laughed as I observed how ridiculous I looked with the pockets bulging with my apparel. It was too late to do anything about it, so I entered the parlor. The inspection team was waiting for me.

Captain Fu was standing in front of the team with a broad smile on his face, as usual. At his side stood Captain Sun. I had come to realize that nothing could go on without this ominous pair. They had become the center of my life, and all my thoughts revolved around them.

Behind these two security officers I observed four inspectors, dressed in blue uniforms. I noticed that each one held a flashlight, hammer, screw driver, and pliers in his hands. Behind the inspectors there was a squad of six soldiers, carrying rifles.

One of the inspectors, short of stature, with inquisitive eyes, stepped out of line and, as he faced me, said: "Sir, we have come to make an official search for broadcasting apparatus."

I was dumfounded as I listened to this short inspector speak in fluent English with an American accent. This was a new surprise procedure. It was the first time that I had been addressed in English by a member of the People's Government, and I remember feeling so uncomfortable that I took a step backward.

The short inspector continued: "Sir, this is a routine which is carried out in all the homes of foreigners in China." He even added: "Be at ease."

I must confess that I still felt nervous.

"Sir," he repeated, as he pulled out of his pocket an official People's Government paper, "here is a search warrant." He held it up for me to read. "You see, sir, we are here on official business." The warrant authorized the inspector to search for broadcasting equipment.

Turning to Ma Chung, the short inspector commanded: "You, Comrade Ma Chung. Go to the kitchen and join the Su family."

Ma Chung was reluctant to go. "If I may have your permission, I would prefer to stay here in the Fathers' company."

The inspector looked at Captain Fu for guidance. Politeness was again the keynote of the evening's performance. I could sense, by the manner in which the inspector had spoken, that nothing unpleasant was to happen.

"Of course, Ma Chung, you may stay here," Captain Fu declared. "I thought perhaps you would prefer to join your own people."

Ma Chung did not answer, but I perceived that he was very satisfied to stay with us. No doubt he suspected, as I did, that perhaps either myself or Father Kent would be politely taken away tonight.

After this was settled, Captain Fu took command. He ordered two of his armed soldiers to go and stand guard at the back door of the rectory, and two soldiers to watch the front door and courtyard; two more were to remain in the parlor.

He nodded to the short inspector to begin the search of the parlor first. Father Kent, Ma Chung and I stood awkwardly in the middle of the room, looking on. Every movement of the searchers indicated that they thought they were on the brink of making some momentous discovery.

The short inspector went to the small table on which I had kept the radio. He picked up the loose wires under the table. His first assistant followed one wire to a base plug, and disconnected it. He solemnly handed the end of the wire to a third inspector who, in turn, wound up the wire extension on a stick and placed it on the table. The fourth inspector traced the ground wire up the side of the wall and out the window. The third inspector strode out the front door, and with the aid of a flashlight tracked the ground wire down the outside wall, where he located the ground rod.

In the stillness of the night I heard the bang of his hammer as he loosened the ground rod. I thought of our neighbors, as the metallic sound of the hammer blows vibrated in the air. I suspected that they were peeping from behind window curtains. They knew that mysterious night searches took place in the town every night among their own people, and that the inspections usually ended with somebody being led to jail.

I knew that the neighbors had testified that Father Kent and I were honorable people. They had been asked, many times, and their answer always was: "The Fathers are good. They help the poor." My neighbors had told me this themselves.

But that wasn't all. One time Captain Fu, talking casually with me, had said: "Father, you know I have asked your neighbors about your character. They all gave the same answer. You are good and help others. Did you instruct them?" I had felt very proud when he told me that. But tonight I was afraid that the neighbors would regret that they had spoken well of us.

The ground rod was firmly buried in the ground. It seemed like an eternity of incessant banging before the noise ceased and the third inspector came inside the parlor triumphantly bearing the ground rod in his two hands. He looked so satisfied at his achievement that I felt as if he had found the instrument that would condemn me as a spy. Each of the other inspectors felt the iron rod in turn.

The short inspector put it on the table, and looked at me as much as to indicate a sort of sympathy that I had let myself be trapped so easily. I yearned to cry out that, after all, it was only an iron rod; but I checked myself, and I noticed that Father Kent and Ma Chung gave me the sign to keep quiet.

Next I saw the short inspector open up a folded ruler and measure the length of the iron rod. He wrote the dimensions down in a notebook. I glanced up at Captain Sun to get his reaction. His ill-omened glance seemed to pierce me. It seemed to me that the electric wires and the ground rod had already convinced him that there was enough evidence to prove I was a spy. I visioned myself hanging from a tree by my thumbs with Captain Sun, pleased with himself, standing under me and looking up at me saying, "I told you so!"

"Sir," the short inspector addressed me, "these wires are an indication that you have operated an electric apparatus."

"We had an ordinary radio," I replied.

"Sir, where is the wave-receiving apparatus now?" he inquired.

"You mean the ordinary radio?" I questioned. "It is in the closet in the dining room."

"Sir, will you fetch it?"

"Gladly." But then I hesitated, for I was afraid to leave the parlor. The thought flashed through my mind that if I left the parlor, they might take Father Kent away. I addressed myself to the short inspector: "May Father Kent go with me to the dining room?"

"Sir, is the wave-receiving set so heavy that it requires two men to carry it?"

"No," I answered. "One man can carry the radio very easily."

Captain Fu read my mind. "Father, you fear evil," he stated. "Don't you realize that the People's Government boasts law and order? No harm will come to you to-night."

I blushed at having betrayed myself and went to fetch the radio. When I returned to the parlor, I set it, dust-covered as it was, on the small table.

"Sir," the short inspector asked, "is this electric apparatus in good order?"

"No," I answered, as I thought of the night Captain Sun had borrowed it.

"Sir, is it registered?" The registration was attached to

it. "Sir, this tag does not state that the radio is out of order."

"It was borrowed several weeks ago." I glanced at the culprit, Captain Sun, but he only leered back at me.

"Sir, have you the receipt?"

I went to my room. As I took the receipt out of my desk drawer, how glad I was that I had not destroyed it! I had the bad habit of throwing receipts, bills and letters in the wastebasket as soon as I was finished with them. Su Wen had been in my room a few days before when I was cleaning out my desk. He caught me in the act of tearing up the radio receipt and had stopped me. How fortunate I was, and how grateful I felt toward Su Wen that night. Without the receipt I would have no way of explaining how the radio had been broken. It was a little thing, but it was the little things that kept me from being hanged.

The short inspector looked at the receipt and was satisfied. Instead of returning it to me, however, he put it in his pocket.

"May I have my receipt back?" I asked.

"Oh, yes. I am sorry. Here it is. You probably won't need it after tonight." I didn't know what he meant to imply by "after tonight," but I understood it to mean that we would be marched off to jail. Had it not been rumored about town?

Back they went to their searching. The next step was for the three inspectors to tap the wall areas of the parlor with their hammers. The inspectors climbed up on chairs and tapped the ceiling. They sounded like big woodpeckers as the sound of the tapping reverberated and escaped through the front door out into the stillness of the night.

It struck me that this part of the performance was put on simply for effect, and I presumed it was done chiefly to impress the neighbors. They tapped every inch of the walls and ceiling with great care, listening for hollow sounds where perhaps the broadcasting set had been hidden by me — a clever, astute American spy. My worry must have been apparent.

"Sir," the short inspector reassured me, as he stopped tapping, "I assure you this is mere routine. Don't disturb your tranquillity."

After the inspectors had tapped the parlor walls and ceiling to their satisfaction, we all moved into the dining room. There was a built-in closet to the left of the door. It was used to store away odds and ends and extra supplies.

"Sir, please open the door."

I did as I was told. On the top shelf were blankets and pillows. The second inspector removed them, and the third inspector helped him to shake the blankets and feel the pillows. A fourth inspector removed a case of washing soap. He tore off the wrapping from one piece of soap and smelled it.

On the second shelf there was a box of nails, a hammer, a screw driver, a wrench, a saw, and a large bundle, or roll, of telephone wire. At the sight of this bundle of telephone wire all the inspectors began to talk excitedly among themselves. They spoke a strange northern dialect, and I could not understand a word they said. I looked at Ma Chung. He knew what they were saying, and he looked excited, too, but of course he could not communicate with me. Then he broke into a smile, and I knew that it wasn't so serious as it appeared to be at first.

The bundle of wire had been purchased several years before. At one time one of the missioners had the idea of setting up a telephone system between the church, gatehouse, kitchen, Su Wen's and Ma Chung's rooms. The idea was dropped, but the wire bundle had never been disposed of.

"Sir," the short inspector inquired, "what are you going to do with several hundred feet of telephone wire?"

The inspectors shook their heads doubtfully when I explained to them the purpose of the wire. I feared that Captain Sun surely would march me off now! A bundle of wire, I thought, would be first-class evidence for him. But nothing happened! The inspectors and soldiers insinuated, however, that they had made a great discovery which in the end would prove that I was certainly a spy. I felt that they were already rejoicing, as it would mean a promotion in rank for them on the Communist table of organization. Perhaps they would be designated "heroes of their country."

Two of the inspectors carried the bundle of telephone wire out to the parlor. I was sure they would parade the bundle through the streets as proof that we were spies. It was a method they used to discredit people. If it wasn't for Ma Chung's smile, I would have broken down.

Later, after the inspectors had gone, Ma Chung explained it all to me. "In their northern dialect they were saying, 'This is very suitable wire to hang these two American spies, but of course we don't have enough evidence. We will make believe we have.'" That was where Ma Chung smiled for my sake, but during most of their performance he looked inscrutable, pretending that he did not know their dialect.

Now they progressed to the bottom shelf where there was a small Pathé projector and a box containing two dozen movie films and a rolled-up silver screen. Beside these was a large pair of field glasses.

Four years before a priest had brought these field glasses from the United States. His brother, who had been in the army in Germany, had given them to him. Sometimes visiting missioners used the field glasses to observe life on the river. As far as I could remember, however, no one had picked them up or removed them from their case in at least two years. But tonight I was embarrassed to see them. Even worse was the fact that on the case was stamped "United States Army."

"Sir," the short inspector said, "are you a member of the United States Army?"

"Of course not," I replied as calmly as I could.

"Sir, what does it say here?" He pointed to the words, "United States Army." He translated the term in Chinese to his comrades. I glanced at Captain Sun. His narrow eyes were focused on the field glasses. I held my breath. Why didn't he come over and take me? I don't understand to this day. Was it because he was looking for something bigger?

Their calmness and matter-of-fact attitude caused me more concern than if they had accused me directly of being a spy. I had never expected to be trapped because of something in the house that belonged to the American Army. I almost despaired, and I wished to surrender. I longed to be freed by the door of death from this mysterious, tantalizing life. Ma Chung could read me like a book. He shook his head, and I checked myself. I realized I had others to think about. I had to fight on, to keep playing the game of pretending.

"Sir," the short inspector said, pointing to the projector, "is this a broadcasting machine?"

Was it possible, I thought to myself, that he didn't know what a movie projector was? He spoke English with an American accent, so I presumed he had studied in the United States. I was confused, but I had enough sense to keep quiet.

"Sir, I have asked you a question, and you have not answered me."

"I am sorry, but I did not understand you," I replied. "This machine is a movie projector." Then I quickly added, "Certainly you are acquainted with moving pictures. They are common in America. From your speech, I conclude that you have been in the United States."

He ignored this remark. Instead, he asked me to set up the projector for operation. This I was very happy to do. What a relief to be in action! While I set up the projector on a table, Father Kent and Ma Chung hung up the silver screen on the opposite wall of the dining room. My night visitors drew up chairs at the side of the dining-room table. One soldier stood guard at the door.

"Do you use this machine to spread false propaganda?"

"I use it to entertain people," I replied.

Out of the films I had chosen a cartoon of Felix the cat and his adventures with a mouse. When I was ready, I signaled to the soldier on guard at the dining-room door to switch off the light. It was a silent film, and my visitors looked on in silence.

Then I began to hear suppressed laughter from my strange audience as Felix the cat and the mouse got into comic situations. At the height of the dramatic action Felix got his long tail caught in a mousetrap which the landlord of the house had placed in a corner to catch the

mouse. Instead, Felix had been the victim! The mouse
clapped his paws and danced with joy on his hind legs
as he saw his enemy in so helpless a condition. Felix
dragged the trap behind him as he tried to run after the
mouse. This was the climax of the film, and my visitors
burst into a loud peal of laughter. Their laughter was like
a tonic to my shattered nerves. My Red tormentors could
be human. I felt sorry for them. They, like Felix, had been
caught in a trap — of Communism. Luckily, it had not as
yet squeezed all the sense of humor out of them.

After the soldier had switched on the light once again,
the short inspector said: "Sir, your machine does not talk.
It is not so harmful as I first thought it would be."

Did he associate the sound track of a projector with a
broadcasting apparatus? I supposed he did, or was he just
teasing me? It was aggravating to be continually mystified.
Anyhow, my night visitors forgot for a moment that they
were in line of duty for the People's Government. In the
end, the projector and the films were carried into the
parlor by the inspectors.

I had often talked about freedom from material goods.
Now I was given the opportunity to practice it. In addi-
tion to the projector, the inspectors took the binoculars,
the tools and the box of soap. I was still worried about the
binoculars. Would the mark "United States Army" in-
volve me as a spy? I was afraid a good case could be made
against me.

Before we left the dining room they tapped every inch
of it in the same manner as they had the parlor. From the
dining room we moved to the library. As the inspectors
tapped the library ceiling, they discovered the trapdoor.
The inspectors and I had to climb into the attic with the

aid of a stepladder. (Between my worries and our afternoons of pitching horseshoes I could now get up more easily.)

The two captains, with Father Kent and Ma Chung, remained in the library. Again I was separated from them, and while I was in the attic the thought flashed through my mind once more that the two captains would take Father Kent and Ma Chung away. At intervals I peeped through the trapdoor to assure myself that they were still there.

The inspectors tapped the whole attic, kneeling to get at corners. They saw all the teachers' manuals, and I was glad we had gone to the trouble of cutting out the objectionable pages against Communism. However, they did not open even one volume, although they had to push them aside to get at the eaves of the house.

In the attic there were two steamer trunks. One was mine and the other Father Kent's. In Father Kent's trunk there were clothing, books and family pictures, and even a pair of horseshoes. These they handed down to Captain Fu. Luckily, he saw no material value in them, nor would they help to make a spy case, so he handed them back to Father Kent.

When the inspectors and I crawled out of the attic, I looked at my wrist watch. It was six o'clock. I glanced out the library window and noticed that dawn was beginning to break over the mountains.

"Sir," the short inspector said in perfect English, "pardon our intrusion. It was a routine duty we had to perform for the safety of our country." He bowed his head and extended his hand to shake mine. At first I hesitated to extend my hand but I realized that, after all, these inspectors — even Captains Fu and Sun themselves — were only doing what they were told to do. The irony of it! After handshaking all around, we parted like a group of friends at a party at dawn. There was no logic in the handshaking. It wasn't even Oriental!

When the inspectors departed the three of us went to church. Happy to be alive and still on the Mission compound, I said Mass with a light heart. Ma Chung served my Mass, then Su Li served Father Kent's Mass, and his mother made up the congregation that glorious morning. I said a prayer of gratitude that we were all still together.

At breakfast the three of us looked as weary as we felt from our night's experience. Su Wen's coffee tasted especially good. We discussed what had happened during the night. It was hard to believe that the inspectors were really searching for a broadcasting set. However, we agreed that the binoculars with their marking, "United States Army," could possibly be made the basis of a conspiracy charge against us.

"We're sitting right on top of a volcano," I said.

"We can't get off now," Father Kent replied. "But if it erupts, we will be blown to Heaven so fast that St. Peter at the gate won't be able to stop us. Then we will be sitting on top of the world. No one ever gets thrown out of Heaven."

17

Father Kent Is a Good Samaritan

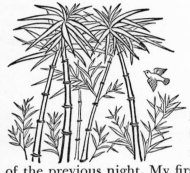

After breakfast I went to my room utterly fatigued from the harrowing search of the previous night. My first impulse was to stretch out on my bed. Instead, I resisted the temptation, and sat in my rocking chair. I was leading a strange existence, and I wanted a few minutes to adjust myself peacefully.

It was a sunny day, and a gentle breeze was blowing from the south. Sparrows were flitting to and fro on the branches of the evergreen tree that was visible from my window. As I watched the sparrows, I envied them their freedom. I would gladly have changed places with them as long as I could be free. It was true, of course, that I was not bound by chains. I had the freedom of the rectory, of the Mission courtyard, and of the church, but I was conscious that I was under constant surveillance and investigation.

Captain Fu and Captain Sun visited me daily. I felt

that they had already tied a rope around my ankles and each day they called on me they had an excuse to wind it higher and higher around my body. I knew what was happening, but I was helpless. It made me angry, but there was no help in that. After all — because of my calling as a missionary — I had freely chosen to remain behind the bamboo curtain.

The slightest mistake on my part would be twisted to prove I was a spy. Now, of all times, I must watch and pray. Again and again I declaimed inwardly: "I am not a spy! I must fight back. I must be prudent and use my wits to prove even to Captain Fu and his comrade, Captain Sun, that I am a Catholic missioner and not a member of the so-called 'United States Spy Ring.' "

Although it was midmorning, my eyes were heavy with sleep. As I repeated to myself, "I am not a spy," I fell asleep in my rocking chair.

The next thing I heard was: "Father, Captain Fu is in the parlor. He wishes to see you." It was Su Wen's soft voice that startled me awake. I gazed at him bewilderedly, running my hand through my thin hair. I was trying to clear my mind and compose myself.

"Are you all right, Father?" Su Wen asked anxiously.

"I am awake now, Su Wen," I replied. "I will go out to the captain at once."

I slipped into my cassock and went to meet my "guest." My very weariness made me angry. I wanted to fight. I was tired of being polite. In the middle of the parlor stood the smiling Captain Fu; beside him stood the sullen Captain Sun. They looked at me like devil twins.

"What do you want?" I challenged.

Captain Fu smiled graciously, as usual. "We have come to ask you to cooperate with the People's Government.

You are requested to permit ten soldiers of the People's army to occupy your parlor for several days, until the barracks are ready at the south end of Tiger Street."

"No!" I answered sharply. "And, what is more, if they move in here I will leave the house and live on the street."

Captain Fu replied with no change of voice: "The ten soldiers will be here at one o'clock."

I had an urge to fly at him, but out of the corner of my eye I saw Ma Chung, Su Wen and Su Li together at the door. No, I thought, I must control myself. I must not get my good people into trouble by creating a scene.

I stood silent as the captain turned and went out into the courtyard. As I watched, the soldiers filed out of Ma Chung's room where they had been quartered and followed the two captains out of the compound.

I went back to the library to break the news to Father Kent. He was hard at work practicing his Chinese calligraphy.

"Soldiers are now going to occupy our parlor," I told him irritably.

"Why are you so disconcerted, John?" Father Kent asked. "Aren't we used to soldiers now? Come to think of it, the soldiers may even 'protect' us from Captain Sun. He won't dare to come privately to take us away at night. It will be a case of the sweetness of adversity."

"Oh, Frank, that's what I call wishful thinking," I replied. "If Captain Sun has anything to say about how we die, he will see to it that the soldiers shoot us in our sleep."

"I suppose so," Father Kent said. Picking up his brush again, he continued to write characters as he remarked with a smile, "We can't live forever, can we, John?"

Sometimes I found it hard to live with a philosopher.

At one o'clock Captain Fu returned with the soldiers. He ignored me completely as he curtly gave directions to the ten soldiers who entered the parlor. They removed their bedrolls from their shoulders and placed them up against the wall. They also loosened their revolver belts and laid them on the floor.

As they made themselves comfortable, Captain Fu disappeared. My good sense told me that it was useless to start complaining to the ten soldiers. They were completely innocent and only obeying orders. It was not reasonable, I reflected, to antagonize them.

As I gazed at them, I noticed that they were all young — all but one, that is, whose gray hair showed under his cap. They were of medium height and were dressed in new green uniforms. It was easy to see that they were wearing these uniforms for the first time. Not only were their uniforms new but also their shoes and caps. They were a quiet, unassuming outfit and, strangely, most of my animosity toward them left me.

As Father Kent noted later, "They came in their 'Sunday best' to be guests of the American foreigners. They had to make a good appearance to uphold the prestige of the Red Army."

After they had finished arranging their things neatly along the wall, they bowed to Father Kent and me in unison. I was surprised, and I glanced at Father Kent as if I expected him to take the lead in finding an answer to this polite action. He looked as mystified as I felt. Then the soldier with the gray hair at the temples spoke up:

"Sorry, Father," he said formally, in a Kwangsi accent, "we will not disturb you."

I had heard another soldier address him as Comrade

Lung, and I could see that he was the leader of the group. I was delighted to hear him speak with the provincial accent. I felt at least we had something in common. Kwangsi was my second home, and it was his native place. All ten soldiers were from Kwangsi Province.

I said spontaneously: "You speak Kwangsi Mandarin! I have lived in Kwangsi for twenty years."

My enthusiasm was quickly dampened as he turned away from me indifferently to order two of the soldiers to go to the kitchen and prepare the evening meal. Two others hung up a blackboard, which they had brought with them, on the north wall of the parlor. Three others squatted on the wooden floor, spread out a piece of white canvas and began cleaning their guns.

I turned to Father Kent and said, "Let's get out of here before we are shot by accident."

When I got to the door, I heard Father Kent call in a low voice. "Look at Leader Lung," he said. Sure enough, the soldier's face had turned pale, and he was shaking. I thought he was about to faint.

Father Kent immediately moved back into the room and put his arm around the man's jerking shoulders. "You are sick," he said gently. The leader tried to push him away. "You have malaria," Kent exclaimed, easing the man down on the floor near his bedroll. As I knelt beside Lung, Father Kent wrapped the shaking figure in the blanket.

The malarial attack was severe, and Lung shook so violently that the whole parlor vibrated. He was in pain, but he did not utter a single moan. He completely ignored Father Kent's efforts to help him.

As I noted this proud coldness, the evil thought flashed

through my mind: Perhaps this is the Lord's way of striking down our enemies! Wouldn't this be a fine method of ridding China of this Red scourge! As soon as I had conceived the idea, however, I was remorseful. This wish wasn't Christian. Nevertheless, with their insolence and craftiness it was all I could do to remember the Communists were human. Even Lung here, a Kwangsi man, wasn't quite human, I thought.

Father Kent got up from beside the sick man and came over to me. "We must do something for this sick soldier, even if we are thrown in jail for it."

Without another word Father Kent went to the end of the corridor. He brought back a cot, sheets, pillows and blankets.

The three soldiers stopped cleaning their guns, and with staring eyes watched us prepare the cot bed for their malaria-stricken patient. Lung was shaking like a leaf. His face was flushed with fever. His eyes were shiny, and he looked miserable.

Father Kent and I eased him out of his uniform and laid him on the cot, tucking him in well.

Lung glared up at us once but I could not tell whether he was grateful or indignant. Father Kent took his temperature. It was 105°. "It's hard to believe his fever has jumped so high in such a short time," he said. But a second reading confirmed it. Looking anxious, he gave the sick soldier two quinine pills to swallow.

"Kent," I said, "it will be a major catastrophe if he bursts a blood vessel. We will be blamed."

"There you are, John. Looking at the gloomy side of things," said he. "Have faith, and let's go to work."

"What can we do?" I asked.

"An alcohol rub, I'd say. It will help to pull his fever down."

We gave him the alcohol rub, and placed cold towels on his forehead. An hour later I took his temperature again. The thermometer still registered 105°. I glanced hopelessly at Father Kent.

"No, it's good news," he said. "At least the fever has not risen any higher."

He gave Lung another quinine pill. An hour later we repeated the whole procedure of rub and pills, then took his temperature again. Kent handed me the thermometer triumphantly. It had dropped a point.

"John," he said, "our patient is out of danger!"

Soon after Lung began to perspire. His chills gradually left him. By ten o'clock his temperature had dropped to 101°.

Father Kent motioned me to help change the sheets on Lung's bed. One of his comrades, rising without a word, brought out from his knapsack a change of underwear.

Lung did not utter a sound all this time. Now, however, his forehead was furrowed, showing that he had a bad headache. Kent placed another grain of quinine and an aspirin tablet in his hand. Lung raised his head and swallowed them eagerly.

"We've done all we can now, John. Let's leave him to rest," Kent said. As we moved to the door, one of the other soldiers called after us: "Thank you, Fathers." It was the first time I had heard that expression from a Red soldier. I was amazed, and noticed that Father Kent was beaming with joy.

With one of my usual changes of mood, I was depressed now that the worst danger was over. Shaking my head,

I said to Kent: "The irony of it is that this very Red leader we have nursed will probably be the one to hang us!"

Kent was too tired and too good-humored to pay any attention to me. With a smile and a yawn he went off to bed.

I went back to the parlor. The soldiers were stretched out on the floor with their feet all converging toward the center. Although the electric lights were on they were fast asleep.

Despondently I went on to my room. We had saved the life of our enemy. He might live to be resentful of having to accept help from a despised foreigner. As I got into bed I recalled Captain Fu's answer when I asked why he was closing down our Mission dispensary, which gave free help to five hundred sick people daily.

"You don't understand, Father," he told me sternly. "Your American medicine heals the body but it poisons the heart!"

18

I Escape the Net
of the Fowlers

I. MUST ADMIT our ten
house guests were little
bother to us. They were neat
and fairly quiet in the house — out early and back late.
The compound was always full of soldiers, so these ten
extra ones made no difference. Leader Lung recovered
quickly. He avoided us, as if embarrassed by the whole
incident.

After a few days of comparative calm, I received a letter
from the People's Bank. I paused before opening the envelope. It could only be bad news about the Mission
funds. Now that both China and the United States were
involved in the Korean War, restrictive steps were being
taken against all Americans in China.

The bank note read: "All American deposits are frozen.
You are requested to appear at the People's Bank in person at eleven o'clock tomorrow."

Anxiously, I went to Father Kent's room to show him
the announcement.

"It was bound to come, John," Father Kent said. "The *Red Star* headlines denounce America every day as the aggressor in Korea."

"That's the reason I hate to go out in the street, Frank. I dread the thought of answering the summons."

"Why, John, you're losing your adventurous spirit. What is adventure but an inconvenience philosophically accepted?"

"I am in no mood for your philosophy, Frank. But, since I must obey orders, I might as well have Su Mei press my clerical suit so that I will look respectable when I make my public appearance."

Next morning at ten I set out for the local police station to procure the first of several passes needed so I could go across town to the bank.

At the police station I showed the announcement from the People's Bank. The clerk wrote out a pass, and, scowling, said in an arrogant manner: "Go home, American!"

This remark from one of the people I regarded as my own stung, like a blow on the cheek. I lowered my head as I stepped into the street. I was tempted to make my way to the bank by the back streets, but recalling my previous encounters on Coffin Alley, I decided to take the broader roads.

I walked timidly along Tiger Street — like an uncomfortable stranger. Yet, believe me, this was the street I knew better than any other in the world!

I was afraid of meeting anyone, friendly or unfriendly. Both spelled danger. Fortunately, the air was heavy with the fragrance of cooked rice. Almost everyone, including the large number of soldiers quartered on Tiger Street, was indoors having his morning meal.

As I passed in front of Governor Wang's house, which had been turned into a military hospital, I saw a group of wounded soldiers basking in the warm sun. I tried to make myself inconspicuous by hunching my shoulders, but, of course, it was impossible.

As I came into view, they began to shout, "American, go home!" They sounded like a cheering squad. People came to their front doors, to ascertain the reason for the vigorous shouting. Recognizing that I was the center of the demonstration, they withdrew, shaking their heads.

Then I saw Su Li across the street and I looked straight ahead. He ran straight to me, however, and clasped my hand.

"Father is a good man," he declared to the world around.

The soldiers seemed to admire his spunk, and just grinned as they repeated: "Go home, American."

"Don't say that to *him*," Su Li admonished them fearlessly.

The soldiers turned away, laughing.

I squeezed Su Li's hand as we walked along together. How grateful I was for his courageous devotion.

"Father, where are you going?" Su Li asked.

"To the People's Bank," I replied.

Su Li hopped along beside me. "I'll go with you. I have to go to the new China Bakery to buy yeast for my father and it's near the People's Bank."

"No, Su Li," I said firmly. "You run ahead. I am a slow walker. Your father may need the yeast in a hurry."

"All right, Father," he answered reluctantly. But he skipped off obediently, pulling out his usual rice cookie from his pocket without missing a skip. Munching it, he

disappeared around the corner on Lion Street. I would
have been delighted to have Su Li for my companion but
was afraid the police would pick him up for questioning.
I didn't wish to get the boy into trouble.

I passed Madame Wu's candy shop, and felt a sad pang
to see it boarded up. What a happy gathering place it had
been for the children of Tiger Street! What a friendly
stopping place for me! Now it was a place of gloom.

When I reached the corner of Tiger and Lion streets a
buxom woman soldier was standing on inspection duty.
I presented my pass hesitantly. First, she peered at me with
haughty, beady eyes, as if I were her personal enemy.
Next, she scrutinized my pass, perhaps hoping to find
something wrong with it. Then, returning the pass to me,
she squared herself and fired at me, like a cannon: "You
old, stupid, idle American fool! Go home."

After her blast I felt like a worm and not a man. I
walked on dismally, finally stopping momentarily in front
of Lin's barbershop. It, too, was boarded up. Moreover,
Lin's picture was nailed to the door, marked: "Wanted."
I guessed that he had fled to the hills. Lin always had been
a very independent person. The last time I saw him, he
told me the barbers' union frowned on him for coming to
trim our hair at the Mission.

"Father, I have come to you for ten years. Can't change
now. Too many regulations, Father. I have always been
a free man."

He spoke the truth, I thought. One did not walk more
than five minutes now without running into a pass inspector.

In the middle of Lion Street a middle-aged soldier was
on duty. I handed him my pass. He leered at me, and made

a motion to tear it. Boldly I snatched it out of his hand. He was surprised and grunted sulkily: "American, go home!"

What a grave predicament I would have been in if my pass had been destroyed! My sense of the precarious position I was in persisted until I was distracted by another sad sight. Yangs' brush-pen shop at the corner of Lion and Main streets was closed! For the past two hundred years Yangs' had made the best brush pens for writing Chinese characters. I remembered its show window where brush pens, used by famous writers, were displayed.

The story of Yangs' was typical of many of the best firms under Communist rule. A new building had been built after World War II. The shop had been prosperous and employed twenty clerks. The first step toward destroying Yangs' had been for the People's Government to open a large brush-pen establishment directly across the street. This government shop undersold Yangs', and gradually they lost their trade.

The Yangs decided to go out of business, but the government ordered them to remain open. The Yangs then decided to reduce the number of clerks, but that also was not permitted. Finally, the Yangs went bankrupt and their business went into the hands of government receivers. Thus this very old house was ruined. As I looked at the fine brick building with the turned-up eaves, the memory of this injustice made me sick at heart.

Suddenly I heard a voice shout: "Halt!" I looked up with a start to see a guard pointing his rifle at me.

Pondering the fate of the Yangs, I had forgotten all about the soldier inspector on every block and had walked by one without presenting my pass.

This soldier was tall and powerful. He towered over me, and snapped the pass out of my hand, shouting violently, "American, go home!"

People passing by became frightened at this outburst and began to run confusedly in different directions. It looked as if a riot had started, and that I was the instigator.

Before I myself realized what had happened I was angry. Was this a conspiracy? Had I been lured out on the street to fall into a trap of insurrection?

I found myself answering back: "I won't go! China is my home!"

The soldier was taken aback at my boldness. He had expected me to take the abuse in silence. Menacingly he leveled his rifle at me. I threw away the caution that I had practiced for so many months.

"Shoot, shoot!" I bellowed at the top of my voice. "If I cannot live in China any longer, at least I will die in China. Shoot, go ahead and shoot!" I cried. I had been cautious too long. I had tried to be the superior man, and not lose my temper. Now, I had exploded like an atomic bomb.

The soldier looked worried. A crowd began to gather round at this unusual sight. A few began to cheer because I was defiant. But when the spectators saw several other armed soldiers come running in our direction they scattered.

Now I was left alone, feeling I had already done more than enough to incur punishment. Strangely enough, the soldiers, instead of apprehending me, waved me to go on about my own business.

As I went on down Main Street, I hardly dared believe I was still a free man. Soon, however, remorse overcame me because I had for a moment thrown away all prudence. How stupid of me to create a scene. But what a relief it was!

Suddenly I felt a tap on my shoulder. I turned around. Two military police stood behind me.

"Who are you?" the first military policeman asked.

"A Catholic priest," I said.

"Are you an American?" the second snapped.

"Yes," I said, putting out my chin, literally and figuratively, "and I am not ashamed of it."

"What are you doing in China?" asked the first. "Spying on the People's Government?" echoed the second.

"That's a lie!" I retorted. We were really pulling no punches now.

"America has invaded Korea," said the first, "and through Korea, she is going to invade China."

"That's false," I told him.

"America is our enemy," the second bore in on me, "and you are an American."

"I am a friend of the people," I interposed.

"Your aviators are killing our countrymen in North China," the first M.P. declared sternly. "How dare you walk the streets?"

"I have a pass," I replied, waving it at him.

The second M.P. pulled it out of my hand. Glaring at it and then at me, he said: "This pass is out of order! You are under arrest!"

"What do you mean?" I asked, astonished. "It was issued at the police station on North Tiger Street."

Again a crowd had gathered around us, and above the tumult I heard some brave soul say: "A shame! Unjust! The Catholic priest is a good man!"

Nevertheless, the M.P.'s started off, marching me between them, like a criminal. We circled around Red Square. The vendors and their customers stopped their transactions to stare at us. As we marched, I felt that his remark about my pass was only a pretext. The arrest must be because of my impudence. I had been too pugnacious.

I put my hand into my pocket and fingered my rosary. How often I had been haunted with the idea that I would be arrested. Now — this was the day — in broad daylight and on populous Main Street. As a matter of fact, I considered myself fortunate, for almost all arrests were secret, in the middle of the night. That spiriting away at dead of night was my real dread.

In a sense, I was even glad something definite was happening to me. In a little while I would be locked up in a prison cell and completely under the control of the Reds twenty-four hours a day. The suspense would be over. It was consoling to think of not having any more surprise visits from Captain Fu and his evil-eyed comrade, Captain Sun. They could no longer prowl our house at night in hopes of catching me in the act of sending messages to America. In jail, I might have some peace of mind.

Suddenly I heard a high-pitched voice call after me: "Father! Father!"

It was Su Li again. Out of the corner of my eye I saw him jerk the M.P.'s sleeve, pleading, "Let Father go. He's a kind man. You have no reason to arrest him!"

One of the M.P.'s angrily turned on Su Li, striking him a severe blow on the head. Poor Su Li went reeling down onto the street. I was alarmed, but Su Li was not to be intimidated by a blow. He sprang up and called, "Father," louder than ever. I did not dare endanger him by answering, but continued to finger my rosary, praying now that no harm would come to Su Li.

In my present wretchedness — discredited publicly before hundreds of curious eyes — Su Li's loyalty was worth more than life to me. Though I could no longer hear him, still I could see his little head wagging from side to side in the crowd, promoting my cause among his companions.

The M.P.'s turned up Coffin Alley, and the carpenters, hearing the noise of the crowd, came to their doors. As they watched me march by, it seemed to me their eager expressions denoted the fact that they considered me a hopeful prospect for one of their largest "everlasting boxes."

It was now past noon, far too late for my bank appointment. I wondered what sort of crime this would constitute.

Finally, we reached the front of a low, gray brick building with a spacious court. A dozen soldiers were on guard at a covered entrance. Su Li and the crowd remained outside, on the street. I heard Su Li start to cry as the M.P.'s led me up a path to the entrance. In my heart I wished to add my tears to his. I had seen the last of Su Li, I thought.

I had heard that the prison behind this military headquarters was intended for special offenders. It was also a very strict prison. Relatives or friends were not permitted to visit prisoners here. They were completely cut off from the outside world.

The guards glared at me as I passed through the large door. They made no remarks as did the guards outside, but their very silence seemed to say, "Give up hope, all ye who enter here."

The M.P.'s led me to a small office. Here a clerk, standing at a counter, filled out a paper and handed it to them. In single file we walked to a double door where another guard was on duty. He took the paper, and motioned for us to enter.

We stepped into a spacious hall. A long, bright table stood in the center of the hall. At it an officer sat writing. He did not look up from his work until we were directly opposite him. Lifting his head, he acknowledged the salute of the M.P.'s. Then he glanced at me. His eyes dropped after a single piercing gaze.

"You may leave," he said to the M.P.'s. Even their rigid Communist training did not prevent one of my guards from drawing a quick breath of surprise at this unexpected order. Obediently, however, they turned and left the hall.

When they had gone the officer did not pause or say a word. He took up his brush pen and scribbled on a piece of yellow paper. He put his seal on this slip and thrust it into my hand. "Go," he said.

I waited for no belated protests from the M.P.'s, but turned and immediately walked out of the hall. The guard at the door inspected the paper. He nodded, and out into the free air I strode.

At the entrance other guards examined the yellow paper. It was a magic token. Out to the path I went, unmolested. Halfway down the street I dared to look around. No M.P.'s were following me. I was free once more. The street was empty before and behind me.

I walked quickly so I would reach the Mission before my luck could change. The winter sun was already dropping behind the mountains. I was free! I was happy! I was alive! Life was sweet! No Bird of Sorrow hovered over me for the moment.

Su Li saw me at the Mission gate. He clasped my hand, sobbing. His father was standing, amazed, at the kitchen window. Father Kent and Ma Chung came running to me from the open door. We all went in together to the library without a word.

Su Li still held my hand. Su Wen brought me a cup of tea. Finally Father Kent and Ma Chung could keep quiet no longer. "What happened? What happened?" they asked. "How did you get away?"

I broke down before I could answer them coherently. Finally I was able to talk. I said: "This has been my worst and best day yet in China. Su Li, your bravery made up to me for all the bitterness of the police. And Frank, at military headquarters, who do you think was officer of the day? Lung, the soldier you saved from malaria. He looked at me, and without a word he gave me a safe-conduct pass and let me go."

"God's grace is everywhere, John," said Kent. "How can we ever doubt it?"

"I still don't understand what technicality they arrested me on," I said. "The M.P.'s seemed positive my pass was out of order."

"Ma Chung knows the answer to that," said Father Kent. "That's why we never expected to see you again. Tell him, Ma Chung."

"This was a plot to get you in trouble. You were told to appear at the People's Bank at eleven o'clock. But what the clerk at the police station did not tell you was that *after* eleven o'clock your pass was no longer valid."

"How did you find this out, Ma Chung?" I asked.

"There was a notice pasted *at noon* on the Mission wall. It read: 'No Pass Held by Foreigners Will Be Honored by the M.P.'s after Eleven O'Clock!' "

What a carefully worked-out trap for me!

And in spite of it all, here I was safe back home. How joyfully I echoed the cry of the psalmist that night: "My soul has been snatched as a sparrow out of the snare of the fowlers! The snare is broken and I am delivered."

Later, after my prayer of thanksgiving, I said another prayer, this time to the Holy Ghost. "Spirit of Wisdom," I prayed, "let Leader Lung think of a convincing reason why he should have let me go free."

19

The Christians
Go to Confession

NEXT DAY Father Kent, Ma Chung and I were in my room making up the monthly payroll for the Mission helpers. "Frank," I asked gloomily, "where are we going to get money, now that the Mission funds are frozen?"

Ma Chung had a suggestion. "I could work for the People's Government as a clerk, Father."

"Yes, John," said Father Kent, "we could all do some work for a living. It might get us out of this house, and the People's Government might not be able to think up a good reason against it."

Just as we were enjoying this pleasantly impossible idea Su Wen appeared at the door of my room.

"Father," he said, "there are some Christians in church who wish to go to confession."

"I will hear them," Father Kent answered, and hurried out of the room.

I stayed to count out the money with Ma Chung. Again I admired his tranquillity. I knew he was unhappy, but he steadily filled in the pay forms for the ration board of the People's Government.

The day for Pan Tao's trial and Li Li's terrible act was now set. Early that morning I had received a green ticket to this public event. It was to be held on the afternoon of the next day, Sunday. Everyone was under pressure to attend. A green ticket, however, meant that one *could* send a representative.

"Ma Chung," I said as we worked, "I have decided to go to Pan Tao's trial myself."

"No, Father." Ma Chung thoughtfully shook his head. "You may run into trouble."

"Ma Chung, I have a green ticket."

"Father, I have a blue ticket. Not even sickness would be a sufficient reason for one to absent himself without a doctor's certificate. I must go."

"Then I will go, too," I answered.

What a purgatory it would be for Ma Chung. How gladly would he have sacrificed his life for Li Li, if only she would refuse to take part in the trial tomorrow.

"Father," he confessed now, "I feel like a reed blown by the wind. In your company, Father, I will find support."

In a little while Father Kent returned. "John," he declared, "the end of the world must be here! The church is full of Christians who desire to have their sins forgiven. Won't you come and help?" I promised, and he immediately returned to the church.

The payroll was finished. Ma Chung picked up the finished forms and prepared to take them to the ration board. I donned my cassock and went over to the church. In the courtyard I met a group of Christians.

"It is strange," I said to them gently, "that so many of you are going to confession this Saturday morning. Is there a parade this afternoon and evening in which you must participate?"

The Christians looked at me in an embarrassed manner.

"It is fine for you to come now or any time it is convenient for you," I added hastily. "I am just curious. I have no other reason for inquiring."

Without giving me any answer they went on into the church.

Su Li and two of his friends were playing in the courtyard. I called them over. "Su Li," I said, "why are so many people coming to confession this morning?"

"Don't you know, Father?" he asked, surprised.

"No, Su Li, I don't."

"Why, Father, our church is going to be officially closed tomorrow by the People's Government."

"What! Su Li!"

"Church closed tomorrow, Father," Su Li repeated sadly as he noticed how upset I was.

I entered the confessional with a heavy heart. But as penitent after penitent came in, I was comforted by the deep faith of our Christians.

Later, I discovered that the Communists' closely guarded secret had leaked out a day or two before. Word had even reached the Christians in the villages around Dragon Town. Some had come ten or twenty miles, had even put up in hotels for the night so as to be on hand Sunday morning for what were to be our last Masses. Somehow they had obtained authorized passes from their respective village officials to come to Dragon Town, and so were not disturbed by the police who made regular rounds of the hotels.

None of our friends had told us the news because they knew what sadness it would mean for us.

Sunday morning dawned a glorious day. As I opened the church door at six o'clock, I realized — now, now it is the last time! The heavy pine door squeaked as I pushed it out against the wall. How many times had I done this before? Now I regretted that so many times I had taken it for granted. The significance of my privilege in being the one to open the door of God's house for so many caused a pain in my heart. After this morning this house of God would be barred for worship. Only by my prayers, perhaps said far away, could I open any doors to Heaven for my people.

My antagonists, Captain Fu and Captain Sun, were already standing outside the church door.

Captain Fu smiled and said: "Good morning," as if nothing important was happening. The irony of the phrase! Captain Sun scowled, but behind his expression, it seemed to me, there oozed a feeling of satisfaction. The Communist clerks had placed tables on both sides of the church entrance. On the tables I saw large registration books, and already some Christians were standing in line to write their names in them. Signing their names in registration books was something the Christians had become accustomed to. They had to do it every Sunday — and it took courage! However, I said to myself, this is the last time this familiar scene will take place at the Mission.

Four soldiers armed with rifles filed into the church. They were the interior guards, posted in the front and the back of the church. In a little while they were lost in the crowd of Christians who entered. Normally, the church could accommodate four hundred but at the four Masses celebrated that last Sunday morning every inch of space was taken. The Christians prayed aloud, and I was touched to the quick by their earnest chant. The last time! The last time! Even in church, in the sight of God, I could not restrain my feeling of resentment at the injustice of the People's Government.

This Sunday I offered the first two Masses, and Father Kent celebrated the last two. During Father Kent's Masses I stayed on kneeling in the sanctuary, praying with our people. How could I miss a minute of this final opportunity? I, who had been their spiritual leader for twenty years, now was praying in unison with them for the last time. How difficult at this moment to bow to God's will. How hard it was, too, to admit defeat. I tried to banish temptation from my mind. Was there really no hope?

What right had the People's Government to deprive our Christians of their religion? Where was the freedom of religion they boasted of? But what use was my indignation? What else did I expect from the People's Government? Did it not proclaim that there is no God, no soul, and a human being is merely an energy to be used by the state?

Now was the bitter end of all our hopes that the Reds would not, in the end, turn out to be so bad as we feared. I knelt in the sanctuary, assisting at the Sacrifice of the Holy Mass offered up by the consecrated hands of Father Kent. This was the hour of worldly failure for me and the hour of worldly triumph for Reds such as Captains Fu and Sun. Looking back, I am ashamed to admit this, but at the time I was tempted to cry out and order the Christians to stand up and fight, instead of kneeling as they were in prayer.

20

Su Li Blows Out the Lamp

WHEN THE MASSES were over, Su Li, having gravely followed Father Kent off the altar, slipped back into the sanctuary still wearing his white surplice and black cassock. For the last time I was seeing him in these garments. What a good altar boy he had been!

Following his usual procedure, he extinguished the Mass candles on the altar and returned to the sacristy. This last time, however, he immediately came back into the sanctuary and, going up to the altar, removed the missal and stand and carried them out.

My eyes followed every move Su Li made. I thought of how graceful and reverent he was around the altar. God bless him. He looked like a cherub. What will happen to him without religion? I asked myself. I took a little consolation in remembering how deep the roots of faith went

in his heart; how fearless he was. I recalled how bravely
he had followed me when I was arrested.

I was just about to rise and go to the back of the church
— steeling myself against the sorrow of farewells — when
Su Li appeared again. He was still wearing his cassock and
surplice, but now he carried a stepladder in his hands. It
was heavy and higher than he was.

Something in the absorbed, deliberate manner of the
little boy kept us all in our seats. We watched him as he
opened the ladder and snapped the hinges on the sides to
keep them firm; then he carefully edged it to the center of
the sanctuary. Cautiously he climbed upward until, reach-
ing the top, he was able to balance himself and stretch out
his hands to touch the bottom of the sanctuary lamp which
was suspended from the ceiling of the church by a sliding
chain. I myself had first lit the lamp on the proud day the
church was consecrated. Never for a moment since had the
lamp gone out — a sign that Christ was ever present on
our altar in the Blessed Sacrament.

With his little hands Su Li drew the sanctuary lamp
down to his level, then solemnly he lifted the red glass
out of the receptacle and brought it close to his chest. Still
holding it in that position between his two hands, Su Li
blew out the light with one breath.

As he slipped the red glass back in the receptacle, a wisp
of smoke curled slowly toward the ceiling. With tears in
my eyes I watched him descend the ladder and disappear
into the sacristy.

Behind me I heard the stir of the congregation. They,
too, were in tears. There was not one of them who had not
been moved by Su Li's gesture and each of us had been

struck by the tremendous significance of his act. The fact that these people were weeping affected me deeply, for I knew that our Christians, like all Chinese, strictly controlled their emotions in public. What a rare experience was this to see the tears of a whole congregation!

The four soldiers on guard within the church were alarmed by the unrestrained weeping. They leveled their rifles. To them, it appeared as if the wailing was but a signal for a riot. Captain Fu, with Captain Sun at his side, rushed into the church. Captain Fu raised his hands in an effort to calm the Christians, but they did not heed him in the least.

With his revolver in his hand, Captain Sun shouted at the top of his rasping voice: "Cease this nonsense of crying and leave the church!" Then he sneered. "Here is a perfect demonstration of the softness of the Lord of Heaven and religion; it makes children out of the adults!"

The Christians paid no attention, and Captain Sun scolded them louder than before: "Stop crying and get out of here!"

I arose, and Father Kent came out of the sacristy to join me. We walked down the center aisle toward the front door. Some Christians pulled at our cassocks to stop us so that they might talk with us. We motioned them to follow us to the front door of the church.

At the door we could only express our feelings by our looks. Our people were being robbed of the expression of their religion, their only real comfort in the bleak world of Communism. Father Kent and I pressed their hands in farewell, saying "Good-by" and "God protect you" to each one. Though the Red officials stood around us, urging us and the Christians to cut short the parting, we refused to be hurried.

Captain Sun's aggravation grew as he watched with envious eyes as the Christians, with great devotion and respect, bade us farewell. At last he exploded, roaring to the Christians: "You think highly of these foreigners, don't you? They are not priests as you think; they are American spies, and they hate you and your country, China!"

James Wang, the young man who was with me at the moment, spoke up without fear: "We have our good priests with us for only a little while longer, so leave us in peace. When the good priests are gone, we will still be here and you can do anything you want with us!"

To my surprise Captain Sun followed James Wang's bold suggestion.

"Good-by," said James as he turned to go. "We have one bond of union forever, Fathers, and that is in prayer."

We nodded, unable to speak.

At noon Captain Fu sealed the church door. I could not bring myself to witness the official act. Su Li was the eyewitness who brought me the news.

21

Li Li Pan Performs a Patriotic Deed

THAT AFTERNOON Father Kent and I were not much interested in Su Mei's good dinner. Our thoughts were torn between the known sorrows of the morning and the unknown sorrows of Pan Tao's trial ahead of us. Father Kent meditatively sipped a cup of tea while I paced the floor, with my hands thrust in my pockets. We had no desire to talk.

Suddenly I lifted my head and asked: "Do you hear the jungle drums?"

"I think I do," he responded.

The sharp sound of the drums was the signal that the procession of the public condemnation of Pan Tao, Li Li Pan's grandfather, was moving northward on Tiger Street. In a short time it would pass in front of the Mission.

Since early morning the Bird of Sorrow had hovered over my head and now I was certain it would nestle in my hair forever.

The boom of the drums emphasized the horror of the impending trial. I began to feel faint and sat down at the dining-room table. Pulling a handkerchief from my back pocket, I wiped my moist brow. Then, overcome, I put my head down on the table. "Frank," I said, after a moment, "to what lengths can one's nerves be stretched?"

He looked at me sympathetically. "Until the mind is completely dark, John, with no ray of hope to urge it to hold on."

"My ray of hope is so dim now, Frank, that I am afraid. Li Li Pan's execution of her grandfather may blacken it entirely."

"John, remember, you have an act of love still to perform. You are the only one who can help Ma Chung. His mental sufferings are far worse than yours."

"You're right, Frank." I arose from the table and began to pace the floor once again. I struggled to control myself and regain courage by reflecting on Ma Chung's plight and how much he depended on me.

As the sound of the drums grew louder, Ma Chung appeared at the door.

"Father, the jungle drums," Ma Chung tried to say calmly.

I watched him and saw his attempt to keep a mask over his feelings. But even though his countenance and body appeared relaxed, the slight tremor in his voice and the movement of his hands betrayed him.

"I hear them, Ma Chung."

"It is time to go, Father," he said reluctantly.

As Ma Chung and I left the dining room, Father Kent said compassionately, "The good Lord be with you!"

Stepping out of the rectory, Ma Chung and I walked

across the empty courtyard. We passed in front of the Mission church. It was the first time I had seen the enormous red seal on the front door.

"Freedom of religion," I muttered. "What a mockery!"

From the Mission gate I could discern the top of the Soviet flag as the procession moved toward us along Tiger Street. At the sight of it my cheeks flushed. How I detested that Red flag and all it symbolized!

"Ma Chung," I suggested, "we will observe the procession from the window in Su Wen's house that overlooks Tiger Street. After the procession has gone by, we can go to the police parade ground opposite the police station at the north end of Tiger Street."

Su Wen and his family were in their kitchen having their first meal for that day. They had been delayed by the confusion of closing up the Mission church. As we all gathered at the window, the first thing we saw was the Soviet flag fluttering in the breeze. It was carried aloft by a color guard at the head of the procession.

I could not help saying under my breath, "Now who is the running dog of a foreign power? This is China and here the flag of Red Russia goes first."

Behind the Soviet flag two soldiers carried a framed portrait of Stalin. The Chinese Communist flag and a portrait of Mao Tse-Tung, Red leader of China, were next in order.

"Father," Ma Chung commented, "that is the man who has brought sorrow to my heart." He pointed to Mao Tse-Tung's portrait. "Li Li Pan is willing to die for him."

A squad of infantry soldiers came into view next. They had a martial appearance, and their rifles glistened in the afternoon sun. These soldiers represented the power of the

Red Army. Behind the spirited soldiers two hundred people walked, four abreast, in semi-military fashion. They were all dressed in blue uniforms. Some were old, with wrinkled faces; others were middle-aged and portly; still others, vigorous adults in their early thirties.

"Who are they?" I asked Ma Chung.

"The residents of Lion Street," Ma Chung replied. "Among the old are some of Pan Tao's closest friends; among the portly are some of his various business associates; the young are members of the rich families of Lion Street whom Pan Tao saw grow up into manhood. Not one in that crowd is in the procession of his own accord. Pan Tao was held in high esteem in his neighborhood."

They all looked sad except a single lean individual at the head of the crowd. He had a cheerful expression on his face and he looked out of place. I asked Ma Chung who he was.

"That is Yao Li," Ma Chung told me in disgust. "He is the one who stirred up the first trouble against Pan Tao. The Red officials appointed him street captain. Father, Yao Li is a traitor, and an ungrateful person. By profession, he is a schoolteacher. It was Pan Tao who paid for his college education. Yao Li, because of his position as captain of Lion Street, has had the Red officials choose him as the master of ceremonies in this tragedy."

As I continued gazing out the window, I wondered which one of the two hundred would be the next victim of the People's Government. I presumed, as I observed their dejected faces, that similar thoughts might be crossing their minds.

Behind the landlords and business friends of Pan Tao I saw girl cadets of the Red Army. They marched with precision and sang Communist songs. As they passed in review, they were singing: "No Communist Party. No China."

At the head of the girl cadets was Li Li Pan. She seemed to be the leading spirit — like a cheerleader — swinging her graceful arms to the cadence of the song. How beautiful and vibrant with life she was! I could not take my eyes off her, nor could I believe that such an attractive girl had the power and daring to do evil. I glanced at Ma Chung. He was seated, staring at the floor. The lines of his face were drawn tight — like a man fighting a temptation.

I knew as I watched that all Ma Chung had to do was to join Li Li Pan in the parade and the gates of earthly happiness would open wide for him. Instead, he stayed here — loyal to Father Kent and me, and to his Catholic faith. Ma Chung was being tried by fire. This was indeed the test of whether he believed that his faith had an eternal value that no human love could equal.

The next two persons in this procession were very familiar to me — my smiling Captain Fu and my obnoxious Captain Sun. Behind Captain Fu's pleasant appearance the lines of cruelty showed, I thought. I suspected that he might be the very one who had instigated the refinement of having Li Li Pan stab her own grandfather, Pan Tao. For a change, sour Captain Sun's features were relaxed. He actually appeared jovial to me. Murder to him, I suspected, was a feast!

Behind the two captains followed eight drummers, two at a time. They were dressed in blue trousers and red shirts. In unison, they produced a one-two, sharp, staccato beat. Immediately behind them fifty young men dressed in blue trousers and white shirts danced to the sound of the drums. Their agile bodies swayed backward and forward, advancing and retreating. They were light on their feet, but their youthful countenances were as serious and solemn as a general's. To me, looking on from Su Wen's window, their rhythmic movements seemed indeed to be a dance of death!

The next tableau cut home to me, too. Here came our own Mission jeep — still bearing the lettering "Catholic Mission, Dragon Town, Stamford, Connecticut, U. S. A." It was the climax of the whole procession.

On each side of it marched two soldiers armed with rifles. The top was rolled down, and in the back seat I saw Old Man Pan Tao. He was bareheaded and looked venerable with his white head and the thin silver beard on his chin. His head was cast down in a fixed position, his slender hands resting rigidly on his knees. He wore a soiled gray gown that gave him an unkempt appearance. Nevertheless, there was still a sad dignity about him.

At the steering wheel sat a burly-looking soldier with heavy-set jaws and thick hands. I noticed that the steering wheel rubbed against his stomach. What, I thought, the representative of the People's Government is fatter than any of us capitalists ever were! Another soldier sat at his side and he, too, was short and stout.

At a distance behind the Mission jeep there followed a crowd of ordinary people who seemed not to be part of the formal procession. They did not march in an orderly fashion but strolled along in groups, talking, and gazing behind them. This motley crowd, I surmised from their behavior, were ignorant of the significance of the procession. To me, they looked like a free people out of Old China. Curiosity was the only reason, I thought, that led them on to follow the death procession of the People's Government. Evidently that government had not as yet reached out to teach them the laws of conformity.

From Su Wen's window I had now reviewed for the first time the Communist march of death. I felt a certain sense of despair in the goodness of man. How many of these people I had known personally. Li Li Pan had been a student in my English class at the Kwangsi University. How many times, too, she had come to the Mission with Ma Chung. I remembered how well she sang. In university entertainments I had particularly enjoyed her comic songs.

Pan Tao, Li Li Pan's grandfather, I also knew well. Occasionally I had sat with him at table at Governor Wang's banquets. During the Sino-Japanese War we had served together on refugee committees. At least once annually he had invited me to his home, usually for a New Year's dinner.

The two captains — Fu and Sun — had been my Red hairshirts. Today I only wished it could be their death march instead of Old Man Pan Tao's! And here, at my side, was Ma Chung, surrounded by tragedy. What was there for him in the Red world? Nothing but ruin.

"Father," said Ma Chung, interrupting my gloomy meditation, "it is time for us to go." I followed him out of Su Wen's house through the courtyard to Tiger Street, where we mingled with the motley crowd. Some of the people recognized me and saluted me. Others asked, "Father, where are you going?"

Ma Chung answered for me. "To the parade ground," and said no more.

In front of Governor Wang's house — now the military hospital — no convalescing soldiers were in view. On the right side of Tiger Street, adjacent to the military hospital, there was a spacious area of level ground that reached to the bank of the Fu River. It was the parade ground of the police corps. It was used, on occasions like today, for the execution of "traitors" such as Pan Tao. Normally, the police corps used the field as a drill ground.

The parade ground had an arch on Tiger Street. From the arch in the four directions of the compass there was a military guard: soldiers in green uniforms, shouldering rifles. Their green uniforms stood out in sharp contrast to the blue clothing of the people assembled for the condemnation of Pan Tao. The soldiers were standing near a platform in the center of the parade ground.

At the arch I presented my green ticket to an official dressed in blue. He was surprised to see me, and wondered why I came when I might have sent a representative. He consulted an officer of the military guard beyond the arch. I recognized the officer. It was Leader Lung again — Lung, who had set me free the day the military police had arrested me.

As the official dressed in blue consulted him, Officer Lung did not look in my direction. He gave a command and the guard returned and permitted me to enter the parade ground.

As I passed through the arch, I suggested to Ma Chung that he mix with the crowd so as not to be seen with me. He said: "No, Father, I need you. Now I am sorely afflicted by a feeling of despair."

We walked across the parade ground and I, too, felt I was in the claws of the Red Dragon! I felt like a soldier on the battleline, with death all around him. By a tremendous effort I overcame my impulse to fear and became daring. I was there only to support Ma Chung and now despair was threatening to fill his soul.

"Come, Ma Chung," I said, "we must get close to the platform."

Ma Chung's eyes flashed wildly at me. I paid no attention to this, but gently elbowed a path through the crowd toward the steps that led up to the platform, which was about four feet from the ground. We found a place near the steps. Ma Chung stood close to me; he had lost his usual self-reliance. This trial of Pan Tao was too near to his own life. How could he reconcile himself to the part Li Li Pan would play in the tragic drama to be enacted before us?

Pan Tao was seated in the center of the platform on a three-legged stool. He was leaning forward with his head bowed. His white beard moved in the gentle wind blowing from the east. He was as still as a statue. Behind him three soldiers stood guard. It was incongruous, I thought, to see the three sturdy soldiers towering over the little, thin, old man.

On the platform to the side stood Li Li Pan between Captain Fu and Captain Sun. Captain Fu saw me standing near the steps. He directed Li Li Pan's attention to me and she glanced in my direction.

Ma Chung, I noticed, was looking over the crowd toward the river. He did not see Li Li Pan look at me, but I felt that her sweeping gaze had taken in Ma Chung also. Li Li Pan seemed to be in constant conversation with Captain Fu. Even now she seemed beautiful. What was going on in her pretty head? Li Li Pan was an intelligent girl; did she not see that she was a tool in the hands of the Reds? How could she stand by so calmly on the platform, knowing the inhuman act she was about to perform? I could think of only one reason. Li Li Pan wished to be somebody — a natural desire of all mortals. And her only chance to be somebody now was in the Red state. Her "patriotic deed" — the murder of her grandfather — would be considered an act of loyalty to the Communist Party and the praise of her name would be on the lips even of Mao Tse-Tung. That would make her "somebody" — famous, renowned, and a heroine of the People's Government.

I observed that Li Li Pan never looked in the direction of Pan Tao as he sat on the stool like a man asleep. I was amazed at the repose of Pan Tao. I had thought that he would be nervous and twist around on the stool. Did he know that Li Li Pan, his own beloved granddaughter, was to be his executioner?

There were three other officials on the platform. One of them was Yao Li, the street captain of Lion Street. Yao Li was to announce the crimes of his benefactor, Pan Tao. The perversity of man's nature! Looking at him, I could detect no sign of sorrow on his face. He appeared joyful. No doubt Yao Li considered it a privilege to be useful to the People's Government.

The residents of Lion Street waited nervously around the platform waiting for the public trial to open.

Yao Li, as master of ceremonies, raised his hands aloft. At this signal the vibrating drums ceased. All of the assembled people turned their eyes in his direction. The atmosphere was electric. I turned alternately hot and cold from sheer excitement. As poor Ma Chung pressed close to me, I could feel his knees shaking. I placed my arm around his waist to reassure and support him.

Street Captain Yao Li began in a deep, resounding voice: "Comrades, it is my honor today to proclaim the crimes of Pan Tao against the People's Government. His two traitorous deeds are: (1) he contributed five thousand pounds of rice to the bandit Nationalist Army; (2) a hundred guns were found concealed on his property.

"As you know, his punishment will be death at the hand of his patriotic granddaughter, Li Li Pan, whom you see standing on the platform."

Li Li Pan stepped forward and pleasantly bowed to the people. How was it possible? She looked joyful, as if she were to receive a medal of honor for her special service to the government. The residents of Lion Street shifted slightly, it seemed to me, to brace themselves for this horrible ordeal.

Next Yao Li declared: "But first the rebel Pan Tao must be punished by you! Each one of you must ascend the platform and slap this reactionary on the face or the head."

The residents of Lion Street murmured as they turned and gazed at one another. This new cruelty seemed to take them unaware. Observing the expressions of dismay on their faces, I began to be worried about myself. Would I have to go up on that platform and strike Pan Tao? Never! I never would!

I turned to Ma Chung. "You won't be asked to, Father," Ma Chung reassured me. "It is only the 'privilege' of the residents of Lion Street."

Yao Li pulled a black notebook from his coat pocket and with his strong voice he boomed out names. One by one they filed past us on their way up to the platform. Some nervously hurried up to the platform; others moved slowly. None of them, I thought, wished to have any part in this shameful proceeding. Some were brave enough just to touch the face of the old man, or the head, in a mere gesture. Others, out of fear, slapped him roundly, signifying their willingness to go along with the People's Government and their hope, by manifesting zeal, to escape punishment themselves. Each resident of Lion Street, I am sure, asked himself the question: "Am I next? Will I be brought to trial and treated like Pan Tao?" It was revolting to watch the life-long friends of Pan Tao strike him on the cheeks one by one.

How did Pan Tao feel about it? Outwardly, the old man showed no sign. His head moved from side to side, according to the intensity of the blows. He did not look up at his offenders; he spoke no evil. He fulfilled the Confucian law: a superior man remains calm under adversity. Some of the blows on his cheek and head resounded sharply. Certainly many were painful, but Pan Tao did not complain.

I detested the ordeal and felt like a coward. Was any decent man not bound to protest? Had I no longer the courage to denounce evil?

Ma Chung must have read my mind, for he pulled my sleeve. I tried to thrust away my angry feelings. I was there to help Ma Chung. This was the great, abominable evil of all Communist tactics. Whenever anyone wished to fight openly for what was right, the realization of how others would suffer made him retreat, to take a compromising attitude. I had come here because of Ma Chung — yet, despite my good purpose, the Reds seemed to be destroying me.

Several times I looked up at Li Li Pan. No doubt she

believed her grandfather deserved to be punished. Was it not his own fault? How did he expect to save himself under the Reds? Was he not a landlord? Had she not urged him repeatedly to flee to Hongkong? Who was to blame? Himself! Consequently, she felt justified in her actions and had no pity for him in her heart.

I looked at Yao Li. What a despicable, ungrateful person. As I watched, Yao Li stepped close to one of the three soldiers and made a sign to one of them. The soldier lowered his rifle, removed the bayonet, and handed it to Yao Li. I noticed that the people were now deathly quiet. Ma Chung clasped my hand — he was trembling violently.

Yao Li presented the bayonet to Li Li Pan. A sigh arose from the people as she took the bayonet. How out of place it looked in her graceful hand! Holding it outstretched, Li Li Pan moved to the center of the platform. She walked up to her grandfather's side. He raised his head, and, for a second, their eyes met. Then he lowered his head, and slumped once more into his listless position. He was a true stoic!

Li Li Pan had inherited this quality from her grandfather. I had seen her excited in my English class, but now she showed complete self-control. Instead of stabbing her grandfather immediately, she came forward to the front of the platform. Was I seeing a play?

Li Li Pan was at ease. She manifested perfect poise as she gracefully strutted to and fro at the front of the platform, pretending to be sharpening the edge of the bayonet on the palm of her hand. Her manner indicated that she was about to make a speech and, like a great actress, she was waiting for the proper moment to begin.

Pan Tao raised his head once again. I noticed that the

soldiers behind him remained rigid. Yao Li, with expectant eyes, was motionless. Captain Fu spoke to Captain Sun, and Captain Sun drew his gun. Captain Fu shook his head, at which point Captain Sun put his gun away. The people standing tense around the platform held their breath.

"What has happened?" I whispered to Ma Chung.

"Father, it is queer — the way Li Li Pan is acting!"

"Look at her, smiling, Ma Chung! If she doesn't act soon, these people will go mad. How long can they stand the strain?" In a few minutes, I thought, the people around me will begin to shout and yell, to relieve their pent-up emotions.

Then at the peak of the excitement Li Li Pan began to make her speech: "Honorable officers of the People's Government, fellow comrades, I have a patriotic duty to perform here which is of tremendous consequence to all of us. It is a great honor for me, as a member of the People's Government, to have been chosen to execute this lofty duty for the glory of New China."

"Long live China!" the people shouted in one voice.

"I have been taught by the People's Government to be honest; therefore, with honesty, I will carry out my noble duty. I am certain that my honesty will bring fame to the illustrious leader of our country — Mao Tse-Tung. I confess it is not easy to be honest, but honest I must be, because I have consecrated my life to the glory of my country!

"Chairman Mao Tse-Tung wishes me to be honest. The honorable officials of our country wish me to be honest. Even my grandfather desires me to be honest. I am certain he is willing to die for my honesty. And you, loyal comrades, assembled here, who look up to me at this solemn hour, also wish me to be honest. Honest I will be, and I hope you will be proud of my honesty and broadcast it to the world. In truth, I am highly honored to perform this exalted duty now."

As quick as a flash of lightning Li Li Pan lifted high the blade of the bayonet and thrust it deep into the floor of the platform. The blade quivered in the sunlight.

I held my breath. Ma Chung leaned against me. Was the thrust of the blade a part of the death ceremony? I asked myself.

The entire crowd was on its toes. Not a sound was heard, but all eyes were riveted steadily on Li Li Pan.

Li Li Pan, standing erect, defiantly continued: "Filial piety is too deeply rooted in my heart. If I destroy it, I destroy myself. I destroy my people. And I destroy my country! Never! I must be honest!"

Captain Fu and Captain Sun — like infuriated wolves in a rage — rushed at Li Li Pan and swept her off the platform.

Captain Yao Li yelled in consternation to the residents of Lion Street, "Do not move!" His shouting was unnecessary, for the people stood stunned, electrified by Li Li Pan's words.

I was also dazed. I tried to move but could not. Ma Chung was holding me fast.

"I am so happy, Father," Ma Chung whispered, tears streaming down his cheeks. "But we must be prudent. Let us get out of here."

He led the way and I followed. I obeyed him mutely, my mind completely occupied with the wonder I had seen with my own eyes.

We were the first in the crowd to reach the arch of the parade ground. No one stopped us as we stepped out into Tiger Street. We hurried homeward at a pace that was nearer a run than a walk. Fortunately, Tiger Street was deserted.

We ran into the library, where Father Kent was reading. He looked up at us sympathetically, then stared. "Why are you two so joyful? Have you lost your minds?"

I rubbed my hands, and Ma Chung kept muttering with his eyes closed. "I am happy. I prayed it might happen as it did. Now I can die a happy man."

"You are acting like two lunatics. Tell me, what is your secret?" Father Kent asked excitedly.

"Frank," I exclaimed, "you won't believe it. At the last minute Li Li Pan bolted!"

Father Kent leaped from his chair and danced around the room. It was something I had never seen him do before, even on the happiest of occasions.

"I am happy, too! I am happy, too!" Father Kent kept repeating jubilantly.

Just then Su Wen entered the library. He was shocked to see us so joyful. "What happened at the parade ground?" he asked. "The people passing by the Mission, returning to their homes, are talking excitedly and are in a cheerful mood. Can murder be committed this afternoon at the parade ground, and these people act gay? What is wrong, Father? Has the whole world gone mad?"

"No, Su Wen," I replied. "The people are sane, God bless them! Li Li Pan rebelled against the Reds. She refused to stab her grandfather. Isn't that wonderful, Su Wen!"

Su Wen's face brightened, too. He cried out: "Father,

it is the happiest news I have heard since the New Order came to power."

Just then we heard three rifle shots in the distance. We looked at one another and then bowed our heads in silent prayer. Old Man Pan Tao, we knew, had been executed by three members of the residents of Lion Street.

Since Li Li Pan had refused to perform the act, the People's Government inflicted on him their usual method of execution for traitors — death at the hands of one's neighbors and friends.

22

Dragon Town, Farewell!

WHAT A DAY this Sunday had been! At ten o'clock that evening Father Kent and I sat resting and thinking in the library. In the morning St. Joseph's Church had been closed by the People's Government — proof that religious freedom was a "big lie" under the Reds. In the afternoon we had seen the miracle of Li Li Pan, a triumph of reason over madness! To me it was a sign of the goodness of man in a world of misery. The thrill of it had taken away all desire for sleep. Nor did Father Kent show any signs of wishing to retire.

"Imagine," I said, "beautiful Li Li Pan in revolt! I hope she will forgive me for misjudging her. Life is sweet to the young but they are the ones who easily throw life away. In battle, it is the young soldiers who die. Here in Dragon Town, Li Li Pan is the first to defy the People's Government in public!"

"John," said Father Kent, "I hear a knock at the front door."

"I hear it, too, Kent. The door isn't locked."

"Shall I go see who's there?"

"No, Frank, don't bother! At this hour you know it couldn't be anyone but Red officials; they know their way around here."

Immediately I heard the door open. "What did I tell you, Kent?" I remarked. Sure enough, heavy footsteps resounded in the parlor and in the corridor. Captain Fu and Captain Sun appeared at the library door with drawn guns.

"What do you want?" I asked the two officers, without getting up. Captain Sun was displeased with my defiant attitude and leveled his revolver at me.

I sneered at him. "Captain Sun, your revolver might as well be empty."

Captain Fu motioned for him to put the revolver away. I remained in my chair as he addressed us.

"You are both ordered out of China immediately. I have your expulsion papers."

"I don't believe you, Captain," I retorted.

He produced two official deportation papers from his coat pocket. He handed one to me and the other he gave to Father Kent.

"You are to be ready to leave St. Joseph's Mission in fifteen minutes."

"Captain, this is nonsense," I exploded. "Surely you can't get rid of us that fast. After all, what is the hurry? Are we not law-abiding?"

"Your passports have expired. They were valid until yesterday. Since your honorable country, America, has no diplomatic relationship with our humble country, China, there is no method by which to renew your visa," he announced unctuously.

We were trapped — aliens without any legal standing, undesirables — and Captain Fu rejoiced.

"In fifteen minutes a squad of soldiers will come to the Mission to escort you to the railroad station," he said. "You are permitted to take with you a small bag containing clothing you may need for travel to the Hongkong border."

"Why don't you shoot me?" I said, as I refused to get out of my chair. "I wish to die and be buried in China."

"We have no orders to shoot you."

"Captain," I asserted ironically, "you could call it an accident."

"Accidents are not tolerated under the People's Government," he retorted.

I slowly got out of my chair. Red legality had finally reached out to snatch me from loyal Ma Chung and faithful Su Wen. I would have preferred a Red jail. At least I would still have been able to remain in China.

I lingered too long in the library. Before I realized it, the squad of soldiers arrived. They pounced on me roughly and ejected me from the room. They clutched my arms, and vigorously shoved me into the parlor.

I shook off my official bouncers, and said in a good-natured manner, "Take it easy. There is no reason for violence. I have not offended you."

Father Kent, dressed in his clerical suit, was standing at the front door. "John, here is your bag."

I turned to Captain Fu and politely said to him, "May I change my clothes?"

"No!" he retorted. "You come as you are!"

I was wearing my cassock.

"You are being unreasonable," I remonstrated as I removed my cassock and, folding it, tucked it under my arm. My departure clothes were now a white shirt and a pair of gray trousers.

"You look more like a sportsman than a cleric," Father Kent remarked.

"Well, at least I have freedom of locomotion for the three-mile march to the railroad station, and that's more important."

The soldiers now pushed me out of the parlor and into the courtyard.

"Captain," I said, "I wish to say good-by to Ma Chung and to Su Wen."

"They are not here," he replied bluntly.

"Where are they then, Captain?"

"That is the business of the People's Government," he asserted in a surly fashion.

The soldiers led me out of the Mission gate onto Tiger Street.

It was as easy as that! In fifteen minutes I had been forced out of the Mission home in which I had lived for twenty years. It seemed to me more painful than a beating or hanging. Mental torture is always greater than physical pain.

I noticed that the sky was clear and the moon and stars sparkled in the dome of heaven. They looked down on a sad, frustrated man as he walked down Tiger Street, flanked by soldiers.

Near Madame Wu's abandoned candy shop I saw a slender figure moving in the shadows. It was a young girl dressed in rags. She held an empty rice bowl and chopsticks in her hands. It was Li Li Pan. She had already become an outcast — a beggar like her father and mother. Slowly she would die of hunger.

"Li Li Pan," I shouted at the top of my voice, "God protect you!"

Captain Sun slapped me across the mouth. I was glad of the hard blow. I repeated my blessing. What a great privilege! My last glimpse of a friend in China was of my heroine, Li Li Pan. I almost became jubilant as I marched between the soldiers. May her name be remembered until the end of time!

When we reached Lion Street, the shops were closed and not one person was on the street. A black cat standing at the entrance to Coffin Alley scampered to a hiding place on hearing our footsteps. I began to be conscious of marching feet. Twelve soldiers armed with rifles kept in step, six on either side of us. Father Kent, carrying a square black bag, was in front of me, dressed in his clerical suit and black hat. His shoulders were square and he held his head erect as he kept in step with the soldiers. Actually, it was the sensible thing to do, but I was still recalcitrant. I purposely slouched and dragged my feet. In no manner did I wish to appear like a soldier. My behavior was aggravating to the guards, who warned me to keep in step with them.

Main Street also was deserted. I felt as if Dragon Town had early curfew that night. Surely, had my friends known that I was being deported, they would have come out to say good-by. The Reds had planned our deportation in detail. On Main Street not even a black cat crossed our path.

At the railroad station they had arranged a different scheme. There was a noisy crowd waiting outside the main entrance of the low, red-brick station. The crowd consisted of students in the youth corps. They were all singing

Communist songs. As they saw us approach, they opened a path for us to enter the station, shouting, "American imperialists, go home!"

In the waiting room the soldier guard dispersed and Captain Fu and Captain Sun approached us. Captain Fu ordered us to sit down. He told us the train was on time, and that our departure from Dragon Town would be in an hour.

Father Kent and I sat in the waiting room, feeling like creatures in a zoo. The students entered the waiting room in pairs and they came up close to stare at us. Like parrots, they pronounced the words, "American imperialists, no good!"

When all the students had expressed their feelings, an official, an inspector of the railroad, came over to us. "Your pass," he demanded.

Father Kent presented the passes to him. He examined them and returned them to Father Kent.

"Now, open your bags," he ordered.

I got down on my knees, laid my bag right side up and lifted the top. Father Kent had packed it for me. On top were my black suit and hat. The hat was crushed, naturally. Next to it was a white shirt and a Roman collar.

The inspector commanded: "Hand me each article of clothing."

I passed the coat of my suit to him. He held it up to the light. He went through my pockets and turned the sleeves inside out; he rubbed his hand over the lining, shook it and then returned it to me. I placed it on the bench behind me.

The inspector looked like a magician. The audience — the students — gaped at him. I handed him the trousers next, and he searched them thoroughly. As he held them up in his hand by the waist, there was a ripple of laughter among the students as one of them remarked:

"See! This American ate well in China. His trousers are very wide! When he gets to America, he will starve and the tailor will have to pull them in."

Red propaganda was now spreading the idea that Americans were starving. Of course these chosen students believed it!

The inspector examined each piece of clothing I had in the bag and displayed it to the spectators. They were very much amused. As I reflected on their simplicity, I became more reconciled to the situation. Gradually I recaptured some of my sense of humor during this foolish procedure.

At the bottom of the bag Father Kent had placed my Breviaries. The inspector saw them and ordered me to give him a volume. I refused, and he bent down and took one himself. He flipped the pages and came upon a snapshot of Ma Chung and Su Li.

"Who are they?" he asked.

"Friends," I answered.

"You have no friends!" he declared. "You are an enemy of China!"

"Father, Father," a high, shrill voice answered. "I'm your friend!"

The students at once turned their heads in the direction of the voice. I recognized it instantly. It was the voice of Su Li. The nimble boy had rushed in and out before my unsympathetic tormentors realized what had happened.

I glowed with satisfaction as I looked up at the surprised inspector. "Do you like my friend?" I asked proudly.

The inspector was too confused to answer. Instead, he

said: "You are not permitted to take out of China any
printed books or pictures."

"These are my prayer books," I argued. "I need them;
and as for these snapshots, they are harmless!"

Of course I spoke in vain. The inspector did not return the Breviaries nor the snapshots to me. What difference did that make? Possessions are not the truly valuable
things in life; loyalty, like the loyalty Su Li had just manifested, was worth more than anything in the world!

The final act of the inspector's part was to hold the
empty bag aloft. He shook it, and since nothing dropped
out, he put it down and ordered me to replace my clothes
in it.

Father Kent had to go through the same ordeal. I admired his patience and aplomb as he carried out the
orders of the inspector. He had the good sense to realize
that a pugnacious manner like mine was futile.

When the train arrived in the station, the student dele-
gation lined up on both sides of the entrance to the train
platform. Captain Fu and Captain Sun led us through the
two columns. We had to run the gantlet of their accusa-
tions:

"Imperialists! Spies! Aggressors! Oppressors!"

On the train platform I looked down at the students
and the two captains below. Captain Fu raised his right
hand and with one strong, determined voice, all the
students shouted: "We will see you in America!"

I opened my mouth to shout back at them, but Father
Kent pulled at my sleeve.

"John, humility is good for the soul," he said softly.
"Come inside and sit down."

I followed Father Kent to a seat and sat waiting for the

crowd outside to quiet down. At last the train began to move slowly out of the station. Suddenly I heard the shrill voice of Su Li once again. It rang through the whole station:

"Fathers, Fathers, God bless you!"

Again he had slipped through the crowd unobserved and found us in the first coach. He stood beneath our window and bade us our last farewell. In spite of our sore hearts Father Kent and I could not help smiling at each other at this last glimpse of Su Li just as the train rumbled out of Dragon Town.

Outside the window the landscape was pitch black. With a surge of hopefulness I turned to Father Kent and expressed what was going through my mind. "The roots of reason are too deep in the hearts of the Chinese people to have them pulled up by this Red madness. Su Li and Ma Chung and Li Li Pan are the real symbols of China — not Captain Fu or Captain Sun."

Taking comfort in this belief, I felt that I could face my long exile ahead knowing that the Bird of Sorrow had not built a permanent nest in my hair and that my people in Dragon Town would one day see the Bird take flight over the hills.